Lament c

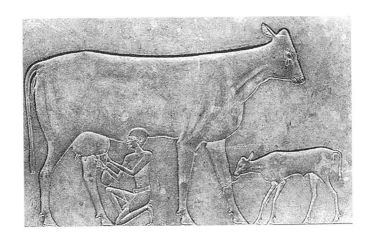

Samuel Baca-Henry

Cover image: Mother cow cries while her baby is tied away from her breast milk. The milk is taken by a human. From the sarcophagus of Kawit, Priestess of Hathor and King's Beloved Wife of pharaoh Mentuhotep II (21st century BCE; 11th Dynasty, first pharaoh of the Middle Kingdom). She is also depicted giving and receiving cow, duck, and other animal offerings. Her husband, Mentuhotep II represented himself as a son of Hathor. He dedicated multiple temples to her, including cow skulls in the foundation offerings supporting the temples. Another of Mentuhotep's King's Beloved Wives, Ashayet, held similar priestly roles in the cults of Hathor and was buried with similar imagery.

samuelhenry@gmail.com | samuel-baca-henry.com

@samuel_lament_of_hathor (IG)

June, 2024

Seattle

This is a work-in-progress.
(feedback/notes very welcome - please email me)

Please contact me for more info and newer versions as this expands.

In order to further spread the message of this book, please consider giving it to someone else when you're done with it.

Please consider donating (or at least following) the animal rights/welfare/liberation organizations listed in the preface.

All images by the author or in the public domain.

Learn more about and *support* animal
welfare/rights/liberation organizations:

<u>Egypt</u>

Animal Care in Egypt

Animal Care in Egypt is a charity hospital dedicated to helping stop the suffering of thousands of animals in the poorest communities of Luxor by providing free veterinary care and education.
ace-egypt.org.uk

Animal Welfare of Luxor

Animal Welfare of Luxor - AWOL - is a small charity providing free veterinary care and treatment for the hard-working animals of the impoverished villages of Luxor's west bank in Egypt. We are the ONLY animal care charity based on the west bank, our services are vital to the well-being of the animals and for the livelihoods of their owners.
awol-egypt.org

Temple Cats of Philae Island

This group advocates, fundraises, and distributes food to the cats who live on the island of Philae, including among the temples to Isis and Hathor.
facebook.com/philaetemplecats

Animal Protection Foundation - Egypt

Animal Protection Foundation (APF) is a non-profit organization and dog shelter registered in Egypt. APF helps the street dogs who have no-one else to care for them. We provide rescue, shelter, medical care and re-homing programs inside and outside Egypt. We also promote awareness, among children and youth and encourage role models who would become inspiring animal welfare leaders within their families, community, clubs, schools and colleges...etc, promote and conduct TNR (Trap, Neuter/Spay, Release) programs to address street pets overpopulation, and endeavor to create animal welfare laws in Egypt.
animalprotection-eg.org

Sudan
Sudan Animal Rescue
Mission: To urgently save the lions in Sudan as well as other vulnerable wildlife.
Motive: To preserve and protect all wildlife in Sudan.
Work: Working with international support teams and local Wildlife Research Department and local officials.
sudananimalrescue.com

Gaza
Sulala Society
Sulala Society is the first and only animal rescue in the Gaza Strip. It was founded by Mr. Saeed Al Err, a man with great love for animals. Unable to bear seeing poor stray animals hungry in the street, he went on daily feeding tours for stray animals since the early 2000s. In 2006, he was able to translate his love and charitable work to the establishment of a registered organisation, Sulala (Arabic for "animal breeds"). Today, Sulala has a dog shelter, a cat shelter, and a donkey.
sulalaanimalrescue.com

Seattle area
Muddy Pug (Maple Valley, WA - 30 min SE of Seattle)
We are committed to educating our community about the plight of farmed animals and empowering people to make the personal choices that save farmed animals' lives. Our residents so often come to us from abuse, neglect, abandonment, or surrender. We are honored to provide them with the food, shelter, love, compassion and medical care they need for the rest of their lives with us.
muddypugfarm.org

Pasado's Safe Haven (Sultan, WA - 45 min NE of Seattle)
Pasado's Safe Haven investigates animal cruelty and provides sanctuary and rehabilitation to animals who have suffered from abuse and neglect. We advocate for better laws to protect animals and work to educate the public about how they can help end animal cruelty. Our programs help save the lives of thousands of animals each year and inspire people to reimagine their relationships with all beings.
pasadosafehaven.org

Northwest Animal Rights Network (Ravenna/Seattle)

The Northwest Animal Rights Network (NARN) is a Seattle-based nonprofit dedicated since 1986 to ending the exploitation of animals by raising awareness of animal suffering in the food, entertainment, experimentation and fashion industries.

narn.org

Animal Rights Initiative (Seattle/Honolulu)

Animal Rights Initiative began in 2017 by a group of Seattle based volunteers hungry for change and determined to get it. We have indefatigably organized hundreds of educational events across the United States, including the 100-Day-Stand against Starbucks' unfair price gouging at their headquarters in Seattle, WA, and the popular "Fur-Free-Friday" events weekly in Honolulu, HI. Beginning in 2019, we expanded our focus to include legislative actions to prevent cruelty to animals.

animalrightsinitiative.org

Note: This book is not affiliated with or endorsed by these organizations.

The author with Hathor at the Metropolitan Museum of Art.
Sculpted circa 1417 - 1379 BCE during the reign of Amenhotep III
(18th Dynasty).

Temple of Hathor at Dendera (about 50 km due north of Thebes
(Luxor) on the Nile)

Temple of Hathor at Deir el-Medina, the restricted workers' village near Valley of the Kings west of Thebes (Luxor)

Temple of Hathor at the desert mining camp of Serabit el-Khadim (Sinai Peninsula, Egypt). Military force was required to control these turquoise mines. Hathor was Mistress of Turquoise.

1840's CE drawing of the ruins of the Temple of Hathor at the desert mining camp of Serabit el-Khadim (Sinai Peninsula, Egypt).

Hathor-headed column at Queen Tiye's temple to Hathor at Sedeinga,
Nubia (present-day Sudan)

Hathor temple of pharaoh Thutmose III in Deir el-Bahari (west of Luxor/Thebes, between the temples of Hatshepsut and Mentuhotep II, both heavily featuring Hathor)

Hathor temple of pharaoh Thutmose III in Deir el-Bahari (now in the Cairo Museum). Note pharaoh Amenhotep II (Thutmose III's son) crouched, nursing from Hathor

Pharaoh Amenhotep II crouched, nursing from Hathor on the statue from his father Thutmose III's shrine to Hathor at Deir el-Bahari, Luxor, Egypt.

OX PILE WITH CAPPING HEAD

OX PILE WITH CAPPING HEAD

*Cow burials from from the Badarian culture present in
El-Hammamiya (Middle Egypt) in the Predynastic Era (circa 5000
– 4000 BCE)*

Cow skull from a foundation deposit at the Hathor temple of Thutmose III at Deir el-Bahari. Humans likely killed this cow by slitting their throat, circa 1430's BCE.

Part One: Hathor Awakens and Summons

The beginning of the recollection of the priestess Hathorhat,[1] Servant of the Goddess Hathor.

Hereafter is Hathorhat's record of the Lament of Hathor:

Hathor Wept[2]

Once it came to pass[3] while I was keeping vigil within her temple at Dendera,[4] in the beginning of the month[5] of her name, while the fertile inundation

---

[1] Meaning "Hathor is foremost".

[2] See the Christian *Gospel of John*, 11:35.

[3] Traditional opening line in Ancient Egyptian literature.

[4] The site of a major cult center of Hathor. The Ancient Egyptian name for the city was Enet-t-neter or "Enet (Home) of the Goddess." It is a multi-millenia site of temples to Hathor, of which the Ptolemaic temple complex remains. It was later converted to a Christian basilica after the Christian/Roman destruction of the Egyptian temples following the Roman empire's backing of Christianity in 324 CE. This came after an earlier period of Roman persecution of Christians, during which, for example, 400 were reportedly tortured and killed on the grounds of the Temple to Hathor at Dendera per Roman policy under emperor Diocletian in the early 300's CE.

[5] Hathor is the third month of the Ancient Egyptian calendar. It lies between November 10 and December 9 of the modern Gregorian calendar. The month of Hathor is the third month of the season of the flood (inundation) of the Nile, which replenished the soil with nutrients and enabled the next season of farming and life.

of the Nile rose towards the temple, that Hathor, our
bovine goddess of the purity and strength of love
and motherhood, mother of Horus, daughter of Ra,
Lady of Fate, mother of the pharaohs, Lady of
Gebelein, Lady of the Sycamore, Mistress of the
Sky and Turquoise, etc., that she wept and the
music and dancing in her temple ceased.

Salty tears and saliva dripped down her cheeks and
lips. She shifted her feet, bent over, and planted her
hands on the ground–they transformed into hooves.
Linen fell from her back to the floor. Hathor's
golden image transmuted into a breathing cow.

The carvings of her on the temple walls wailed and
lamented.[6]

In the dark holiest center of the temple where she
had once stood resplendent yet hidden, I cupped her
chin in my palm. Tears collected around her eyes.
She cried a soft and desperate low through her open
mouth. Frustrated breaths warmed my hand.

*As I tried to comfort her, I thought of all she had
done.*

---

[6] See Maimonides (13th century CE Jewish rabbi, philosopher,
theologian, jurist, commentator, and physician to Saladin),
Guide of the Perplexed, Book III, Chapter 29.

She births Horus every dawn. The celestial goddess
Nut takes on a bovine form to carry Hathor's father
Ra through the sky each day. Ra fills Hathor, Lady
of the Vulva, every evening so that she may rebirth
the gods and goddesses with the morning sun's rise.
She guides him through the Twelve Gates every
night.

*Faience mummy pectoral adornment of the goddess Nut; circa 1070
– 664 BCE; Third Intermediate Period or later*

Once, her vengeful father Ra sent Hathor as his Eye
to destroy humanity for rebelling against him. Thus,
she became Sekhmet the ravenous lion despite her
gentle nature. Nearing their extinction, Ra finally
relented and spared humanity from such reckless
fury by tricking her with 7,000 jars of blood-red
beer. She became drunk, slept, and ceased the
rampage he instigated. Upon awakening, she was no

longer Sekhmet and returned to her loving form as Hathor.[7]

She and Horus of Edfu created their child Ihy, half-brother of the pharaohs, god of the sistrum rattles heard in the music-making at temples and festivities.

Now Hathor laid down. She sighed a mournful sigh.

The cow Goddess Bat on top of the Narmer Palette, depicting Narmer's unification of Egypt and the founding of the First Dynasty, 31st century BCE. Hathor eventually subsumed much of Bat's role. Narmer is shown destroying city walls and vanquishing his enemies in the form of a bull. Egyptian pharaohs were sometimes referred to as Strong Bulls, or Bull of His Mother.

---

[7] See the Ancient Egyptian mythological literary text, *The Book of the Heavenly Cow.*

Note the four Hathoric heads of the goddess Bat on Narmer's belt (see next image)[8]

Note the four Hathoric heads of the goddess Bat on Narmer's belt

[8] Note that *Pyramid Text* spell 546 says "My kilt which is on me is Hathor." See Gillam, p. 215.

Narmer as bull on the palette

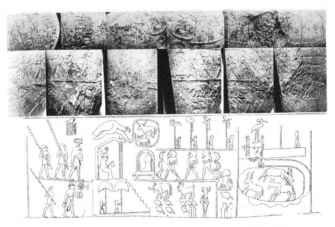

Ornamental macehead of Narmer (circa 3100 BCE)

Narmer, the first pharaoh to subjugate all of Upper and Lower Egypt combined,[9] knew that his strength came from the capture and exploitation of hundreds of thousands of cows from his adversaries.

He celebrated and honored Hathor's predecessor cow goddess Bat on his commemorative palette illustrating his rule of Upper and Lower Egypt. On

---

[9] Some time around 3273–2987 BCE.

this palette he showed himself as a raging bull, destroying his enemies' walls and cities.

The cow goddesses and living cows became the source and sustainer of the god Horus and the herdsman-conqueror pharaohs.

Sneferu[10] violently seized at least 20,000 cows and 7,000 people from Nubia.[11] He captured at least 13,000 cows and 11,000 people from Libya. Many of them died on their way to forced labor and slaughter in Egypt.

Hathor had been dear to the pyramidist Menkaure[12] and his family. He commissioned many temples for her. She stood by his side to protect him in his statues to solidify his legitimacy over the nomes[13] of Egypt. After him, the pharaohs Userkaf and Sahure relied on associations with Hathor as their mother and wife.

---

[10] Circa 2613 to 2589 BCE.

[11] *Palermo Stone*, section 147. Translated by J. H. Breasted in *Ancient Records of Egypt, Volume I.*

[12] 2532 – 2504 BCE. Pharaoh who commissioned the smallest of the remaining three great pyramids at Giza.

[13] A nome is an administrative region governed by a Nomarch. Menkaure commissioned at least five statues depicting himself with Hathor and the relevant nome goddess of the given nomes.

Hathor protecting the pharaoh Menkaure. On her right, the Hare Nome goddess of Khemenu (aka Hermopolis) offers an ankh of life in her left hand

Menkaure's pyramid at Giza

Shrine/outer sarcophagus of Sadeh, a wife of pharaoh Mentuhotep II and Priestess of Hathor. Note the slaughtered cow above the door and the herded mother cow and calf in the bottom right.

Stela of Intef, Overseer of a fortress in Herakleopolis within the administration of Mentuhotep II. Herakleopolis was the seat of the rivals of Mentuhotep II and the Theban dynasty during the First Intermediate Period, before he conquered it and re-established control over all of Upper and Lower Egypt

Mentuhotep II[14] claimed Hathor as his mother to legitimize his reunification of Upper and Lower Egypt after a period of division and war. He dedicated a temple to her at Gebelein, where she had already been worshiped for centuries as the Lady of that city, known also as Per-Hathor (House of Hathor). He depicted himself suckling[15] Hathor's udders in her shrine connected to his temple at Deir el-Bahri across from Thebes. Several of his wives

---

[14] Died 2009 BCE. His reunification of Upper and Lower Egypt marked the end of the First Intermediate Period and the beginning of the Middle Kingdom.

[15] Hathor is at times equated with Isis, who suckles her son Horus. The pharaoh is known as "the Living Horus." This iconography showcases the pharaoh as the child of the goddess(es).

served as priestesses of Hathor. Yet these queens depicted bound and slaughtered cattle in their tombs and on their sarcophagi, buried within this mortuary and cultic complex abutting the western mountains in which Hathor dwells; from which she emerges. Near his and Hathor's shrines, Mentuhotep II buried many of his most effective soldiers who helped him subdue and re-unite Upper and Lower Egypt.

Hathor nursed the great pharaoh Hatshepsut[16] as a child, which she commemorated at her temple. Thus with Hathor as mother and Amun as father, Hatshepsut ruled as king. Yet there was a herd of sacred cattle at this temple who were raised to have their legs tied together, be thrown to the floor, and have their throats slit to honor the pharaoh and Hathor. Flesh of the goddess's children were buried in tombs to feed the humans in their afterlife. So also with ducks, geese, fish, and honey. These smells bloomed around the valley. The funeral trains were pulled by Hathor's sons, who were then slaughtered in sacrifice after dragging the sarcophagi and other offerings to the tomb. Hatshepsut's name would later be erased from the temple she dedicated to Hathor at Gebelein and many future king lists.[17]

---

[16] Reigned as pharaoh from 1479 until her death in 1458 BCE.
[17] See Takács, et al, 2015.

Hathor nursing the pharaoh, 19th Dynasty (perhaps Seti I), circa 1295-1186 BCE

Tiye[18], the Great Royal Wife of Amenhotep III[19] and mother of pharaoh Akhenaten[20] continued this representation as Hathor. Tiye's temple to Hathor at Sedeinga[21] in Nubia declared her to be the image of Hathor, just as her husband became Amun and their son became the Aten. This identification of the ruling queen with Hathor was customary among the Nubians and so provided legitimacy.[22] This benefited Tiye and her husband, as well as their children. She continued to dress in tribute to Hathor

[18] Circa 1398 – 1338 BCE.
[19] Died circa 1353 BCE.
[20] Died circa 1336 BCE.
[21] Within present-day Sudan.
[22] See Dr. Ashby's talk The Goddess Isis and the Kingdom of Meroë.

even after her son promoted the Aten as primary god to be worshiped instead of or above all others. After her husband Amenhotep III's death, Tiye and Hathor protected him in his next life.

Hathor-headed columns, Temple of Mut (associated with Hathor); Jebel Barkal (contemporary Sudan); A plateau mound in the desert; Sacred to many cultures of the region, including Kerman+Kush+Egyptian+Bedouin+(all of the above)+more .

Gold-leafed copper alloy sun-disc headdress from a figure of Hathor or Isis. Found in Kerma, Nubia (present-day Sudan) in the Late Period.

Meroitic beaker found in Faras, Nubia (present-day Sudan)

Many of the pharaohs' wives and children served among Hathor's priestesses and priests.

And so these and the other pharaohs and their families had relied on and served Hathor.

Now Hathor closed her eyes. She clenched her dripping lids and darkened her world.

Ptolemaic era plaque of two Hathors assisting a woman in childbirth (circa 4th to 1st century BCE)

Of humans, she had stood beside the wombed to try to protect during childbirth. In the form of the Seven Hathors, human fates were determined as newborns. Later, Hathor helped the deceased move to the Duat–land of the afterlife. And she greeted them with bread. Seven more cows and their male consort, who some say is Osiris, Lord of the Cows, assist the deceased according to the Book of the Dead. The cow called She of Chemmis nurses the deceased with her milk.[23] Thus Hathor and her brethren aid humans seven times with their births and seven times with their rebirths; and also for the gods.

Now Hathor was silent. She slept. Her great lungs heaved.

I kept vigil over her through the night, gently stroking the Mother of mothers like my babe, as she had comforted and nuzzled so many.

She turned her head to the left and saw a pile of severed cow forelegs on an offering table amongst cakes and flowers. To her right she saw a pile of cow heads on another offering table amongst sacrificed birds and red-soaked linen. She laid her head upon the offering table and wept, filling its indentations with her tears. She snorted and gritted her damp eyes as she reared away from these. The smells of charred flesh and incense lingered in the air from the day's burnt offerings.

---

[23] Pinch, 178.

Hathor shook off the four remaining ceremonial cloths that we had put upon her. She stamped on them like one threshing grain. She tore them with her horns and teeth. She shredded them as one lamenting.

I walked slowly alongside her. Instead of rising to the rooftop to greet her father Ra as every other morning, we exited the temple. We made our way around its inner yards and corridors. Her hooves pounded a dirgeful beat on the stone floors. We passed piles of glass, pottery, wooden carvings, faience, beads, and stone offerings to Hathor. Some were in the form of cows. Others depicted an ear—that she might hear the supplicant's petitions. Amidst these were amulets, necklaces, bracelets, and rings. There were also hanging painted linen tunics depicting the goddess. Hathor nosed at these before continuing outside.

As we passed through the pillared entrance hall, the sparrows and bats who made their homes in its higher places swooped down to accompany Hathor outside.

The day was still night. Sopdet, the brightest star in the sky, looked down upon us.[24] The goddess Nut

---

[24] Sopdet was the Ancient Egyptian name for the star Sirius, the brightest in the northern sky. The star's rising coincided

waited in vain for the sun so she could carry Ra and spread the rays of the Aten sun-disc across Egypt between her horns. None could see their own nor our shadows,[25] for they saw darkness by day.[26]

The priestesses, priests, and others were afraid and surprised to see the one who shines as gold. They were used to yoked cows goaded and whipped by their custodians. And they had seen Hathor's statue floated up the Nile to visit Horus at Edfu, south of Thebes. But they had never seen something like this.

They feared the darkness and Her Brightness.

I obediently followed Hathor as a child following her mother.

We continued outside the temple to its cowpens. Here were cows held by the temple and its priestesses and priests, who were themselves mostly born of royalty, the palace, the temples, and other elites. These were rented out for the temple's profit to be worked on lands owned by the temple itself.

---

with the beginning of the annual flooding of the Nile. It was associated with Hathor (and Isis). She is equated with Sopdet at times (see Temple of Hathor at Dendera).

[25] A person's shadow, or *Shut*, was considered part of their soul. It accompanied them to the afterlife.

[26] See the *Stela of Neferabu* for this phrase.

Some from this herd were hobbled and sacrificed–offered to the goddess Herself, as well as to other deities, including the pharaoh. [27]

They mooed when they heard us, likely hoping it was breakfast time.

Near the cowpens were burial pits containing some of their kin. An in-progress dig lay open, with the corpse of a cow lying recumbent[28] next to it. Hathor gazed upon this body. I laid a lotus flower[29] under the cow's nose and mouth. Hathor walked back to an offering table inside to get beer and bread. She placed these next to the cow's head. She stood over him to try to nurse this rotting cow. His tongue hung limp from his dead mouth. Hathor nuzzled his face.[30] She sighed before turning back towards the pens.

Hathor kicked down the fences and stood among her brethren. She mooed back to them and they

---

[27] Note: the cow species (Aurochs; *Bos primigenius*) appearing within this book has been killed to extinction by humans from their former wild lands spanning central Asia to north Africa and Europe. They were domesticated into and replaced by the contemporary cow species *Bos taurus* and *Bos indicus*.

[28] Like the seven cows in the *Book of the Dead.*

[29] A symbol of rebirth.

[30] She is trying to greet and sustain the slaughtered cow as she is described assisting recently deceased humans in the *Book of the Dead.*

gathered around. She licked their faces and they licked hers. All rubbed their great heads together.

A calf walked around her seven times before lapping the tears from Hathor's left eye. The calf called out for her mother, who ran over to nuzzle and suckle her babe. The little one lapped up the milk which she had lately been deprived of so that it might be offered in the temple instead. Another calf approached, but was unable to reach these cool tears and warm milk because of the nose ring he was pierced with for weaning and painful control.

Beyond the cowpen and entrance pylons, the inundating Nile flowed before us. The moonlight of Isis shimmered over the waves.

Hathor Summons

Then spake the pure one Hathor, Lady of the
Sycamore, Mistress of the Sky and the Turquoise,
Lady of Love, who gives life to all living things:

> Hathorhat, my priestess – Please summon to
> me[31] Neith and her son, my father–Ra.
>
> Summon Isis and Osiris, parents of Horus.
>
> And my son with Horus–Ihy.
>
> Invite Renenutet from Terenuthis. With her
> ask Nehebkau and Geb. And Sobek Nepri,
> and Meretseger, She Who Loves Silence.
>
> Bring Anubis, Montu, Bastet, Amun, Nut,
> Mut, Ammit, Hesat, Nekhbet,[32]
> Mehet-Weret, Taweret, Satet, Anuket, Bat,
> Ihet, Bata, Seth, Thoth, Ma'at, Tjenenyet,
> Raet-Tawy, and Imentet, as well as their
> high priestesses and priests, if they have any.

---

[31] Mirroring the summoning language used by Ra in the *Book
of the Heavenly Cow* prior to being convinced to have his
daughter Hathor destroy humanity for not following his ways.
[32] Known as The Great Wild Cow of Nekheb (an early
dynastic Egyptian city).

Bring me the 42 Assessors of Ma'at, who include Thoth, Nehebkau, and Sobek.[33]

And bring the Pharaoh and the Royal Wives and all the children of the Pharaoh's body.

Bring me the Viziers of Upper and Lower Egypt, all the Nomarchs,[34] and the Overseers and Counters of the cattle.

With care, bring the sacred living Apis, Buchis, and Mnevis bulls. And with care bring the living parents, siblings, and children of these bulls. Let them be transported on their gold-stalled[35] barque ships. Bring me also the Ba-souls[36] of the

---

[33] The 42 Assessors of Ma'at judge the souls of the dead in the afterlife. Books of the Dead instruct the deceased how to pass their tests by denying having committed specific sins. Ma'at was the god of truth and order.

[34] The Kingdom was divided into sections called Nomes. Nomarchs were appointed to govern these territories on behalf of the pharaoh.

[35] See Diodorus Siclus, The Library of History, Book I: section 185, for a description of the transport of newly identified Apis bulls after the previous one's passing to the West and becoming Osiris-Apis.

[36] The Ba is the personality part of the soul. It was depicted as the person's face with the body and wings of a falcon. It is unknown whether the ancient Egyptians believed that non-human creatures (such as the sacred Apis bulls) were outlived by Ba-souls. The Buchis bull was considered to be the living incarnate Ba of the god Ra (father of Hathor). So Hathor is challenging this theological relation of the Buchis

former sacred bulls who are already buried at Saqqara alongside their parents. Summon also the courtiers of these Osiris-Apis, Osiris-Buchis, and Osiris-Mnevis bulls.

Now therefore call unto me all the prophets of my temples, all my servants, and all my priestesses and priests; let none be wanting: for I have a great complaint.[37] Bring them

bull to Ra, instead implying that the Buchis bulls had their own personal Bas separate from (or in addition to) Ra's.

[37] See *2 Kings*, 10:18-29: "'Therefore, summon to me all the prophets of Baal, all his worshipers, and all his priests: let no one fail to come, for I am going to hold a great sacrifice for Baal. Wherever fails to come shall forfeit his life.' Jehu was acting with guile in order to exterminate the worshippers of Baal. Jehu gave orders to convoke a solemn assembly for Baal, and one was proclaimed. Jehu sent word throughout Israel, and all the worshippers of Baal came, not a single one remained behind. They came into the temple of Baal, and the temple of Baal was filled from end to end. He said to the man in charge of the wardrobe, "Bring out the vestments for all the worshipers of Baal"; and he brought vestments out for them. Then Jehu and Jehonadab son of Rechab came into the temple of Baal, and they said to the worshipers of Baal, "Search and make sure that there are no worshipers of the LORD (Yahweh) among you, but only worshipers of Baal.' So they went in to offer sacrifices and burnt offerings. But Jehu had stationed eighty of his men outside and had said, 'Whoever permits the escape of a single one of the men I commit to your charge shall forfeit life for life.' When Jehu had finished presenting the burnt offering, he said to the guards and to the officers, 'Come in and strike them down; let no man get away!' The guards and the officers struck them down with the sword and left them lying where they were; then they proceeded to the interior of the temple of Baal. They brought out the pillars of

from all the Nomes of Egypt, along with the
Overseers of the cows of the temples.

And bring me millers and generals and
musicians and doctors and dancers and
builders. Summon to me fishers and farmers
and fowlers and masons.

Let these be brought so that they may be
judged.[38] And invite the enslaved peoples of
Dendera but let them travel here freely only
if they choose.

For now, let the day remain dark over you.[39]

Hathor sent also for cow goddesses and gods from
distant places so we could hear how the cows are

---

the temple of Baal and burned them. They destroyed the pillar
of Baal, and they tore down the temple of Baal and turned it
into latrines, as is still the case. Thus Jehu eradicated Baal
from Israel. However, Jehu did not turn away from the sinful
objects by which Jeroboam son of Nebat had caused Israel to
sin, namely the golden calves at Bethel and at Dan."

Note: All translations from the Tanakh/Hebrew Bible are from
the Jewish Publication Society (JPS)'s 1985 translation.
[38] See *The Contendings of Horus and Seth*, in which the
Ennead council of the gods tells Hathor: "Let Horus and Seth
be summoned so that they may be judged."
[39] See *Micah* 3:6, "Assuredly, it shall be night for you. So that
you cannot prophesy, and it shall be dark for you, so that you
cannot divine; The sun shall set on the prophets, and the day
shall be darkened for them."

treated amongst them. She hoped that all would be well among them and sent her greetings.

She sent up the Nile for her priestesses in Nubia and Meroë, where she was also called Atari.[40] She invited representatives of the Medjay herding peoples, who buried their leaders and loved ones with painted cow, goat, sheep, and gazelle skulls. And she invited Kerman people from Nubia, who were sometimes buried with hundreds of cow heads.

Cow-decorated stela from Kerman tomb in Nubia (present-day Sudan)

---

[40] □□□□ in Meroitic. See Rowan, "Meroitic - A Phonological Investigation," p. 50.

From Meroë, capital of the Nubian Kushite Kingdom between 591 BCE - 350 CE. Present-day northern Sudan.

Votive cow (bronze & gold) found in Byblos (present-day Lebanon) at the Temple of Baalat Gubal (Lady of Byblos – with whom Hathor is sometimes identified).

From Byblos. Note the Hieroglyphic name of Hathor (bird within the square–meaning "House of Horus")

Byblos (present-day Lebanon) at the Temple of Baalat Gubal (Lady of Byblos – with whom Hathor is sometimes identified).

We dispatched speedy emissaries, delegates, and priestesses east to invite the Bull of Heaven at Sumerian Uruk.[41] These would first sail to Kebyny via the Wadj-Wer.[42] After the ships were moored to the shore,[43] they would visit the temple of Baalat Gubal, where Hathor was worshiped in the form of the Lady of Byblos[44] in this land of cedars. It was in Byblos where Isis reclaimed her husband Osiris's corpse from the coffin his brother Seth tricked him into.

---

[41] Present-day Iraq.

[42] Egyptian name for the Mediterranean Sea. Means "Great Green."

[43] A phrase from the magician Djedi in the *Westcar Papyrus.*

[44] Lady of Byblos is a translation of Baalat Gubal, which may be a proper name, a title, a description, or a combination of all of the above. Throughout Egypt (and Byblos), Hathor sometimes has the epithet Lady of Byblos. Baalat Gubal was also sometimes associated with Astarte, Anat, Aschera, Aphrodite, and Isis. See Zernecke 2013.

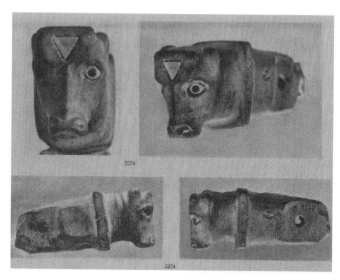

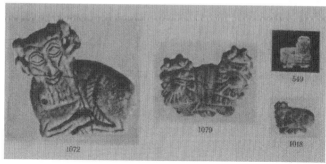

From Mari (present-day Syria)

From Byblos, some of our people went southward
through Retjenu[45] to learn about the gods and
treatment of the cows there en route back to Egypt
by land. Others departed Byblos via the road to
Mari via Qatna. Next they would board ships to sail
down the river Buranuna[46] to Uruk.

After Uruk, these would travel to Persepolis to
request the primordial bovine Gavaevodata. His
soul Goshorun had lamented[47] the bovine fate to the
Zoroastrian god Ahura Mazda.

We sent messengers aboard departing Keftiuan[48]
trade ships returning across the Wadj-Wer to request
their Sacred Bull and the Minotaur (his son with
Queen Pasiphaë, wife of King Minos). And we
would seek representatives on behalf of the rest of
their cows. Hathor would protect the ship and its
navigators on their journeys.[49]

---

[45] Ancient Egyptian name for Canaan and Syria.
[46] Euphrates.
[47] See *Yasna 29* of the Zoroastrian scriptures. In this Gatha
poem, attributed to Zarathustra himself, the Soul of the Cow
(*geush urvan*) laments on behalf of all the cows that they exist
in the forceful fury, bondage, violence, and vice of humans.
The great god Ahura Mazda (Divine Wisdom) proclaims that
the prophet Zarathustra will transmit the divine teachings of
goodness through poetic song and thus champion and save the
cows. https://lrc.la.utexas.edu/eieol/aveol/10
[48] Keftiu was the ancient Egyptian name for Minoan Crete,
present-day Greece.
[49] See Colonna 2018, p. 75.

These seaborne delegates would continue to Pylos
and then the isle of Helios,[50] to invite some of the
Sacred Herd of their sun god. Next they would
invite the cow goddess Io. Finally, they would go to
Croton[51] to request the Sacred Ox of Pythagoras the
vegetarian.[52] Among these messengers were some
who had studied alongside Pythagoras himself at
Egyptian temples. While in Croton, they would call
on the priests of the Cult of Mithras to send
delegates and explain their rites.

Because she could not summon from times yet to
be, Hathor requested the prophetess Neferti[53] to tell
of the future condition of the cows and of any
potential saviors among humanity or gods.

Hathor instructed with a sweet, deep, lovely voice:[54]

---

[50] The island was sacred to Helios and guarded by Helios'
daughters Lampetia and Phaethusa. Also called Thrinacia.
Sometimes identified with Sicily or Malta.
[51] City in present-day southern Italy.
[52] The philosopher and mathematician Pythagoras allegedly
studied with Egyptian priests before returning to Greece. His
followers practiced vegetarianism. The ox itself was
convinced by Pythagoras not to eat fava beans since these
contained the souls of the dead. The ox was subsequently
tended to and worshiped in Tarentum near the temple of Juno.
[53] See the *Prophecy of Neferti.*
[54] See *Lotus Sutra.*

Ensure safe passage for all on their journeys.
Go without chariots. Go without donkeys.
Do not force horses to carry them or oxen to
pull them and their supplies. Send
accompanying doctors with skills to treat the
animals and the humans. And instruct your
overseers not to beat the sailors and others
who help them in their journeys.

Shu,[55] my brother of the body of Ra – please
provide steady winds so that those going by
sea are carried directly. Things carried by
the wind do not break the backs of animals
or people.

It is to this cowpen[56], among my brethren,
that you shall summon them. Of those
among these who have names in their own
ways, let my scribes record them.

Hathor again closed her eyes and was silent. Her
fellows in the cowpen encircled her for protection.
The day was still as night outside the temple and
throughout all that Horus could see. Cattle dung
burned for illumination.

---

[55] Primordial god of wind, dry air, who separated earth and
sky. He and his sister Tefnut are the parents of Geb (earth god)
and Nut (sky goddess).
[56] See *Atharvaveda*.

And so we summoned all she requested. Some of these we summoned with spells to visit from the past. And all with spells to quicken their travels and arrivals so that they were as swift as a body's shadow.[57] As it was dark, we enlisted the Barque of Hathor's father Ra to transport some of these with speed and safety, sailing across that Nile of the sky.

---

[57] See *The Book of the Heavenly Cow* for the "swift as a body's shadow" phrase in the context of Ra's runners sent to fetch red ocher dye for him to make red beer to get Hathor (in the form of Sekhmet) so drunk that she will stop executing his order to destroy humanity.

From the circa 650 BCE tomb of Mentuemhat, a priest of Amun at Thebes in the Kushite Nubian 25th dynasty of Egypt (and Nubia)

A scared calf (carried by person on right) looks back for their mother while fording water in a marshland

Marsh scene from the pyramid of Userkaf, pharaoh in the early 25th century BCE. Note the hoopoe bird (center-right) with the head crest.

Part Two: Hathor Illuminates

Arrivals

Those summoned began arriving, and these were positioned on either side of her, touching the ground with their foreheads so that she might state her problem in their presence.[58] These were the goddesses and gods and pharaoh, the royal families, and priestesses and priests. And the millers and generals, governors of nomes, rulers of armies, and people of the Nine Bows,[59] both under the yoke and free.[60]

The living cows of the de-fenced temple pens remained with Hathor. The Apis, Buchis, and Mnevis bulls and their parents, siblings, and children joined these. The cow-headed winged Ba-souls of their deceased family members perched in the sycamore trees around us. Flies and gnats buzzed. The land still lay in darkness.[61]

---

[58] Mirroring the arrivals of Shu, Tefnut, Geb, and Nut, Nun, and the gods who were present in the primeval abyss after being summoned for Ra in the *Book of the Heavenly Cow*.

[59] The Nine Bows are symbolic representations of the foreign enemies of Egypt.

[60] See *Lotus Sutra*, Chapter 1.

[61] See *The Book of the Heavenly Cow* for the phrase "So the land lay in darkness."

Also assembled and sitting together in congregation
were thousands of beings not human: baboons,
gazelles, oryxes, ibises, falcons, frogs, crickets,
horses, leopards, donkeys, ticks, giraffes, cats,
jackals, butterflies, hippopotami, sheep, ducks,
snails, deer, dogs, elephants, egrets, termites,
geckos, ostriches, lions, gnats, crocodiles, hyenas,
hartebeests, vultures, hedgehogs, mice, antelope,
heron, falcons, scarabs, worms, ants, bats, geese,
kingfishers, herons, dung-beetles, rabbits, bees,
skinks, desert foxes, doves, swallows, acacia, irises,
cormorants, kestrels, pelicans, weasels, gerbils,
praying mantises, hoopoes, warblers, partridges,
eagles, flamingoes, quail, shearwater, curlew,
turtles, flies, great serpents and snakes including
vipers, adders, mambas, and boomslangs. Even the
scorpions came.

As it was the third month of Akhet, the inundation
brought to the temple many puffer fish alongside
medjed, mullets, catfish, tilapia, and yet more
hippopotami and crocodiles. Aboard some of these
crocodiles perched sandpipers. The frogs praised
the inundation.[62] Kites landed around the deceased

---

[62] See *The Instruction of 'Onchsheshonqy*: "It is the frogs who
praise the Inundation. It is the mice who eat the emmer. It is
the oxen who bring about the barley and emmer. It is the
donkeys who eat them."

cow and sang to his body.[63] And pigeons from nests all over the world came to hear Hathor's message.

Horus sailed down from Edfu on his barque. Hathor herself, in her aspect Lady of Gebelein, sailed down in her sacred barque. Osiris descended from his roof shrine atop this very temple at Dendera. Isis, Nephthys, and Imentet swooped down and gathered with the kites guarding the dead cow.[64]

The cow's winged Ba soul alighted next to the body and spread his wings to Isis and Nepthys. They shrieked and cawed with the cow's Ba, who cried out and then collapsed.

A hundred thousand or more winged Ba-souls of sacrificed ibises lined up like an army to listen.

---

[63] Trying to revive him as Isis and Nepthys did for their father Osiris with their magical songs in the *Lamentations of Isis and Nepthys.*

[64] As they protect Osiris's corpse in the *Lamentations of Isis and Nepthys.*

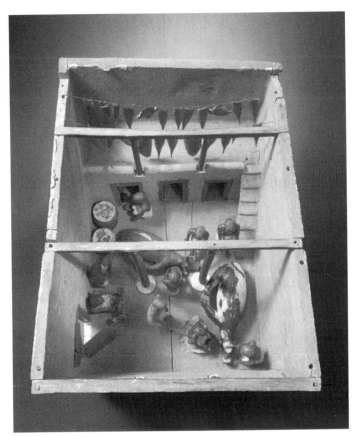

The slaughterhouse model of Meketre.

He was Chancellor and High Steward (provider of food to the royal palace) to the 11th Dynasty pharaohs Mentuhotep II, Mentuhotep III and perhaps Amenemhat I (Late 2000's – early 1900's BCE).

Cattle census (biennial cattle count) model of Meketre

Pre-slaughter fattening stable model of Meketre

63

*The golden calves of Jeroboam, King of the Kingdom of Judah, who
commissioned them for temples in the cities of Bethel and Dan.*

Jeroboam sacrificing to one of his golden calf statues

The hieroglyph name of Hathor.
From the temple of Baalat Gubal in Byblos (present-day Lebanon)

Status of cows, sacred cows, and cow goddesses and gods of other peoples

Hathor asked if we had news of the cow goddesses and gods she requested from other lands.

The priestesses and priests from Kebny raised their gold braceleted arms[65] in praise of Hathor, their Baalat Gubal, the Lady of Dendera who dwells in Byblos.[66]

Yahweh accompanied our messengers who traveled southward through Retjenu after departing Byblos. Also from Retjenu came Jeroboam and Amos from the kingdoms of Israel and Judah. Jeroboam had dwelt in Egypt before, seeking refuge under the Meshwesh[67]-descended Egyptian Pharaoh Shoshenq I after a failed conspiracy to usurp King Solomon, who had built the great temple in Jerusalem. Solomon had also built temples to the gods Moloch and Chemosh. The Queen of Sheba, near Punt, taught Solomon the languages of the birds, the ants, and the bees.

---

[65] See Montet, Item 32, page 57 for a description of their golden bracelets from a statuette found in the Temple of Balaat Gubal in Byblos.

[66] See Colonna, 2018 for this epithet.

[67] Ancient Libyan Berber tribe.

Shoshenq I made war against the Kingdoms of Israel and Judah. He looted the temple of Solomon. After Solomon's death, Jeroboam returned to the Kingdom of Israel and took the throne. Then he built temples with golden calf statues in the cities of Bethel and Dan to mitigate the power of the temple at Jerusalem in the rival Kingdom of Judah. Already sacked by the Egyptians under Shoshenq I, this temple would later be destroyed by the Neo-Babylonians.

The prophet Amos from the Hebrew Bible, as drawn by Gustave Doré
(France, 19th century CE)

Amos, a shepherd and sycamore[68] fig gatherer, objected to Jeroboam's golden calves and was thus banished from the northern Kingdom of Israel back to his native Kingdom of Judah. There were, however, some even within the Kingdom of Judah who constructed bronze bulls, as at the Bull Site in Samaria. In addition to his advocation of Yahweh worship only, Amos spoke the words of Yahweh to the Israelites, warning that Yahweh does not accept the burnt offerings, meat offerings, and peace offerings of the unjust. Yahweh told through Amos of the destruction, flooding, and famine of the people of Israel for their evils. And that this would be accompanied by the darkening of the earth on a clear day. As it was yet still dark, Amos was frightened and panicked.

---

[68] The sycamore tree is sacred to Hathor. She is the "Lady of the Sycamore." Some coffins were made from sycamore wood. Thus, the Hathoric tree encased the deceased's body in preparation for their eternal rebirth from her womb in the afterlife.

The prophets Amos, Zechariah, and Malachi from the Hebrew Bible

Zechariah icon, painted circa 1654 CE; from the church of St. John
Korovniki in Yaroslavl, present-day Russia

A man named Zechariah had joined our delegates in Samaria. Here in the dark he comforted Amos. Zechariah told us that Yahweh commanded him to feed and care for the flocks that had hitherto been kept for slaughter, especially the weakest among the animals. Zechariah reported that their former keepers considered themselves blessed by Yahweh for the riches that the sacrifices paid them. And these considered themselves not guilty though they slew their flocks.

The goddess Qetesh came with them, riding upon a lion. This lion and Hathor's form Sekhmet laid together peacefully in the cowpen. From Retjenu came also these gods and their courtiers: El, El Shaddai, Ba'al[69]-Hadad, Anat, and Asherah. We had heard of Asherah from correspondence with the Amorites, especially their king Abdi-Ashirta.[70] Some even said that Yahweh was married to Asherah. She, Ishtar, and Astarte commingled. Astarte's cow-skin sandals had worn out from the

---

[69] *Judges 2*, 2:11-13: "And the Israelites did what was offensive to GOD. They worshiped the Baalim and forsook the ETERNAL, the God of their ancestors, who had brought them out of the land of Egypt. They followed other gods, from among the gods of the peoples around them, and bowed down to them; they provoked GOD. They forsook GOD and worshiped Baal and the Ashtaroth." Ashtaroth is sometimes equated with Astarte/Ishtar/Inanna.

[70] "Servant of Asherah". See Amarna Letters 60 and 61.

journey.[71] Some saw Astarte as their Queen of
Heaven Innana, called Ishtar.

With El came Eliphaz the Temanite, hungry,
wandering, and looking for bread. He knew that the
day of darkness had been readied for him.[72]

Among these were three sets of twin brothers. One
pair of brothers were devoted to Astarte. The next
pair of brothers were devoted to Innana. The third
pair of brothers were devoted to Ishtar.

Innana had sent the Bull of Heaven to his death by
Enkidu and Gilgamesh. Amongst the Egyptians she
was said to be the daughter of Ptah and a wife of
Seth, along with her sister Anat.[73] Some even
believed Hathor and Anat were related in sphinx
form. But the Hittites called Inanna Šauška (Ištar of

---

[71] As the sea god mockingly asks her about her journeys across
heaven and earth after she has been summoned by the
Egyptian harvest goddess Renenutet to deliver tribute to quell
the sea's anger in the Egyptian story *Astarte and the Insatiable
Sea*. Šauška plays the role of Astarte in the Hurro-Hittite
version, *Song of the Sea*.
[72] *Job* 15:23: "He wanders about for bread—where is it? He
knows that the day of darkness has been readied for him."
[73] See *Astarte and the Insatiable Sea* (The Literature of
Ancient Egypt, ed. Simpson, 2003. See also *The Astarte
Papyrus and the Legend of the Sea* by A. H. Sayce, 1933.

Nineveh), whose image their king Tushratta sent to protect the ailing pharaoh Amenhotep III.[74]

On the road to Mari, we camped with an army returning with 3 talents of gold, 100 talents of silver, 300 talents of copper, 300 talents of iron, 1,000 copper vessels, 1,000 brightly colored garments of wool and linen, the conquered enemy's daughter and her large dowry, 20 talents of purple wool, 500 cows, and 5,000 sheep.

Sacrificial procession scene from the Royal Palace of Mari, present-day Syria (circa 2500 - 1800 BCE)

Our messengers stopped in Mari, the cult center of Astarte-Ishtar, and saw them sacrificing cows. These were born with the help of the seven divine Korharat midwives, then slaughtered before they had seen seven or eight cycles of the moon.

---

[74] See *Amarna Letters 19 and 23*; cuneiform-inscribed clay tablets found at the Amarna (Akhetaten) palace of pharaoh Akhenaten. In *Letter 23*, Tushratta requests that the statue of the goddess be returned.

Cows were also slaughtered for Ḥepat, the wife of Hadad among the Canaanites and Mesopotamians, wife of Tešub among the Hurrians, and wife of Tarḫunz among the Luwians and Taru among the Hattians. Before placing them on the offering table, they would divine messages from the liver and the heart. Sometimes they offered male cows and sometimes the females.

Hathor-headed ivory plaque from Assyrian Kalḫu (aka Nimrud; present-day Iraq), circa 8th–7th century BCE. May have been captured or sent as tribute after Assyrian domination of Phoenicia.

Bull hunting scene from Ashurnasırpal II's palace at Assyrian Kalḫu
(aka Nimrud; present-day Iraq) circa 883 – 859 BCE

A lyre from the Royal Cemetery at Ur circa 2500 BCE

En route to Ur, this group of our messengers stopped next in the great Assyrian city of Kalḫu. There, they were amazed to see images of Hathor among their prized objects. However, they found out that these had been carried away from Phoenicia by the force of conquest.[75] The Assyrian army covered their siege engines in wet animal skin to prevent the defenders from burning them. Along with the sacred images, the Assyrians captured and brought home valuable animals and women.

---

[75]The Neo-Assyrian king Esarhaddon, son of Sennacherib, father of Ashurbanipal, who lived in the safety of Kalḫu, would conquer Egypt in 671 BCE.

Mesopotamian goddess Ereshkigal wears the divine horned crown and stands upon two lions. Circa 19th-18th century BCE. Possibly from Ur (present-day Iraq)

Upon learning this, our messengers decided it best to move on. They exchanged gifts and greetings before some continued southward to Ur to seek the Great Bull of Heaven and then on to Persepolis to seek the Zoroastrian primordial cow Gavaevodata.

Zoroastrian priests arrived with our messengers from Persia giving word that after 3,000 years of peaceful living, their primordial cow Gavaevodata was slain by Angra Mainyu–the destructive evil

force. This evil one also cut down the pastures.[76]
Gayōmard, the primordial human, died thirty years
later from his wounds during the same attack.

Goshorun, the soul of Gavaevodata, lamented her
fate and the ill-treatment of cows and other animals
to the god Ahura Mazda. This god foretold the
eventual coming of a prophetic protective savior for
all the cows and all creation. The poet-herdsman
Zarathushtra would ensure pasturage with Rightness
amidst many sunbeams for the cows of all
creation.[77] And he rejected the usage of cows' fat in
the sacred haoma drink among his people.

Grains and medicinal herbs were born from
Gavaevodata's body. And his sperm gave birth to
the first bull and cow, ancestors of all the species.
The same also happened with Gayōmard seeding
the first human parents.

The gathered Zoroastrians now rose up to heaven
and enjoined Mithra, protector of cows and
pastures, to descend and look over Hathor and all at
the cowpen. Mithra, accompanied by his
poet-singers and the curious Assyrians, gathered

[76] See *Yasna* 32 of the Zoroastrian Gathic hymns of
Zarathushtra.
[77] See the above-mentioned *Yasna 29* and *50* of the Zoroastrian
Gathic hymns of Zarathushtra as well as Chapter 4 of *The
Bundahishn* for another lament of Goshorun.

here now around a pile of cow dung and lit a fire.
When a white male cow began to urinate in the pen,
some collected the urine in a metal bowl. They
placed the fire and a bowl between stones on which
laid various utensils. They gathered water from the
temple well and placed it in another bowl next to
the urine. Now they began reciting their sacred
poems.

This lasted about seven hours. The twenty-ninth of
their poems said:

> The cow's soul lamented to you, the gods:
> "For whom did you create me? Who
> fashioned me? Cruelty, oppression,
> bloodlust, rage, and violence have fettered
> me, and there is no herdsman for me other
> than you. Therefore, you must all show me
> the way to good pastures."

> Then the cow's Fashioner asked Truth:
> "What was your allotment for the cow when,
> ruling the earth, you all gave her
> cow-tending nourishment together with
> pasturage? Whom do all of you desire as the
> Lord who would destroy the cruelty wielded
> by the Possessor of the Lie?"

The one who is not a slayer of the alliance with Truth and is free from hatred for the cow would reply to him: "One is not to know of those things by which He drives the lowly to lofty heights. But he to whom I shall go, on account of his having sent out requests for aid, will be the strongest of beings."

Zarathustra answered: "The Wise One is he remembering best the pacts that, indeed, he has made with daevas[78] and men sometime before now. And those also that he will make sometime later. He is the discerning Lord; it will be for us just as he would wish."

Zarathustra continued: And so, then, do we two–my soul and the fertile cow's–devote ourselves with zeal, with hands stretched out to the Lord, so that we may dispose the Wise One to answer our inquiries. Is there no prospect for the cattle-breeder living justly among the Possessors of the Lie?"

So the Wise Lord, the Knowing One, speaks the solemn words inspired by his insight: "There is no lord found by even one among

---

[78] Deities.

us, nor a paragon in accordance with any Truth. Alas, the Fashioner has fashioned you for the benefit of the cattle breeder and the herdsman.

"The Lord who is allied with Truth fashioned the magic formula for procuring butter and milk for the cow. This Wise One is beneficent towards the emaciated in accordance with the teaching. Who is there for you who might set these things down for mortals by Good Mind?"

Good Mind said: "There is this one found here for me who alone hears our holy teachings–Zarathustra Spitama: he wishes to recite praises for us and for Truth, O Wise One, if I shall give to him sweetness of voice."

And so the soul of the cow laments: "I who am to accept a powerless provider, a weak man's voice which I wish to be strong–When during my lifetime will he emerge, the one who lends to him a helping hand?"

Zarathustra said: "O Lord, may you give strength to them through Truth. And that power, which comes through Good Mind, by which one may receive comfort and peace. For I myself, O Wise One, know You as the Primordial Provider of that."

The Cow replied: "Where are Truth, Good Mind, and their power? Know me, through the mortal one, You, O Wise One, in Your concern for the great offering. Come down to us now, O Lord, on account of our gift for those like you."[79]

After reciting their poems, the Zoroastrians took a pinch of ash from the dung fire, rubbed it in their hands with some of the consecrated urine, and pressed it to their lips. And they collected some hairs that had fallen from the cows. They wrapped these around their rings.

---

[79] Translated by Scott L. Harvey, Windred P. Lehmann, and Jonathan Slcoum at the University of Texas at Austin Linguistics Research Center.

Kamadhenu

Kamadhenu

Illumined by fire, the Zoroastrian Mazda-worshippers introduced the Hindu goddess Kamadhenu[80] from Goloka, the heavenly world of cows.

Govinda, the Protector of Cows, arrived soon after with Krishna, the young cowherd of Goloka.

Arriving now with these came Nandi, the bull of Shiva. Though not a god himself, Nandi accompanied Kamadhenu and now laid in the temple cowpen amongst the Apis, Buchis, and Mnevis bulls. Humidity was in their eyes.[81]

All of these laid down, letting tears run over their chins.[82] Isis, the mother of the Apis bull, stood guard before these.

We were pleased to meet Kamadhenu of India. She stood over a termite mound and released some of her milk to nourish their tireless colony.[83]

---

[80] Also known as Surabhi.

[81] See the *Lamentations of Isis and Nephthys* for this phrase meaning their eyes were full of tears.

[82] See the Zoroastrian *Hymn to Mithra*.

[83] See THE CONSTRUCTION OF A CULTIC CENTER THROUGH NARRATIVE: THE FOUNDING MYTH OF THE VILLAGE OF PUTTAPARTHI AND SATHYA S̄Ā̄I B̄Ā

Kamadhenu, having overheard the Zoroastrians' recitation of the Cow-Soul's Lament, recounted her own lament to the King of the Celestials, Indra. While Indra wandered the earth, Kamadhenu's tears fell upon him. Indra looked up and beheld, in the sky, the afflicted Kamadhenu, weeping piteously. His first thought was that this might be a premonition of some future calamity. The wise Kamadhenu patiently answered:[84]

> O Devaraj,[85] you have no cause for fear, I am afflicted on account of the suffering of two of my sons. See, how wretched they are, how wasted and oppressed by the sun's heat! O Devaraj! The ploughman has struck them cruelly! Born of my body, I am filled with grief to see them yoked to the heavy plough! Verily nothing is dearer to a mother than her son.[86]

Rather than seeing to the welfare of the cows, Indra was instead only motivated to free the captive human prince Rama so that his mother would not be distressed. He didn't even unburden these two that Kamadhenu specifically mentioned. He had known

---

[84] See *Ramayana*, chapter 74. Shastri, 1952.
[85] King God.
[86] ibid.

his sister[87] Kamadhenu's cows had fallen down by
the way and yet ignored them, not even helping her
to lift them up again.[88] Indra, having known of this
suffering, and certainly powerful enough to stop or
prevent it, had done nothing to help the cows.

Some of these offered prayers to Rudra as well.

At Keftiu,[89] we learned that the sacred bull had been
seized by Herakles for the Mycenaeans. The bull
later freed himself but was recaptured by Theseus
and killed in Athens to gain favor with Zeus,
Athena, and Apollo. Theseus then traveled to Keftiu
and killed the Minotaur. Keftiuan priestesses sailed
back with our messengers and now arrived at the
cowpen. They mingled here among their
counterparts. We heard how their flocks and
families were rotting on the peaks and coasts of
their great island. Famine, flood, Mycenaeans, and
even fellow starving siblings had brought death
among all.

The sun-god Helios came in the absence of his
sacred cattle we'd invited. They had been slain and

---

[87] Kamadhenu is a spouse of Kashyapa, father of Indra (with
Aditi as mother).

[88] See the law in *Deuteronomy* 22:4 "If you see your fellow's
ass or ox fallen on the road, do not ignore it; you must help
him raise it."

[89] Crete, present-day Greece.

eaten by companions of the evil-starred king of Ithaka.[90] Helios arrived commanding a horse-drawn chariot across the sky. Hathor nuzzled him in condolence. She then nuzzled his horses, lamenting their bondage by this god who loved his cows and sheep yet oppressed his horses.

Our emissary to Croton reported that the Sacred Ox of Pythagoras had been slain along with the peaceful Pythagorean vegetarians and the philosopher himself.[91]

Our emissary to Croton recognized among the Persians Mithra of wide pastures [92] We learned he had been perverted by the Romans into a bull-slaying cult. This had spread throughout the Roman-dominated lands, and might spread even to Egypt if the Romans invaded.

Musicians and singers of all the gods from all the lands stood mute.

---

[90] In *The Odyssey,* Odysseus's men slay and sacrifice the sacred herd of Helios to try to get a favorable change in weather so they can depart the isle where they've been held by a storm sent by Poseidon.

[91] Around 509 BCE. Some accounts state that Pythagoras himself almost escaped but refused to trample a field of fava beans that lay in his path and was thus caught and killed.

[92] See the Zoroastrian prayer Khwarshed Niyayesh (Litany to the Sun). It was to be recited thrice daily.

All who arrived were present within fourteen days. It was now the middle of the month of Hathor.[93] The moon shone all night and day in a downward crescent. The inundated Nile kept flowing. Moonlight illuminated the cows drinking at the shores.[94]

---

[93] This was a festival day in the Hathor cults. See also the Sahidic Coptic Christian apocryphal Life of Mary, which places Mary's birth on the 15th day of Hathor. Mary's parents are depicted as wanting a child to inherit their wealth in gold, silver, and cattle.

[94] Hathor is identified as "Uniting with the Left Eye, brightening the Banks" (the moon/light west of the Nile) at Dendera.

Hathor Illuminates & Addresses

Now Hathor raised her eyes and in a moment there issued a ray from within the circle above her head. This ray sent forth light in the darkness which surrounded her.[95] It extended over all the nomes of Upper and Lower Egypt so that every field and desert appeared wholly illuminated by its radiance.[96]

The ray extended into Libya and Nubia as well as the eastern and Sinai deserts. It shone among the cedar trees near Byblos[97] and across the lands of the Levant. The islands of Alashiya[98] and Keftiu[99] in the Wadj-Wer[100] saw the rays of the dawning of

---

[95] See *Book of Gates*, Sixth Division, #12 in which Ra addresses a group of gods (including Hathor) who convey souls and make provisions for the dead. These are gods "...who send forth light in the darkness which surrounded you...."

[96] See Lotus Sutra and The Theology of Hathor of Dendera: Aural and Visual Scribal Techniques in the Per-wer Sanctuary, p. 65, by Barbara Ann Richter.

[97] Hathor became associated with Baalat Gubal (Lady of Byblos), the primary goddess of this coastal town in present-day Lebanon. This goddess was sometimes seen as an incarnation of the Semitic and Hittite fertility goddess Asherah, the Ugartiic and Amorite goddess Anat, and the Mesopotamian/Akkadian/Babylonian/Assyrian/Hittite goddesses Astarte/Ishtar/Inanna/Šauška.

[98] Present-day Cyprus.

[99] Present-day Crete.

[100] Egyptian name for the Mediterranean Sea. Means "Great Green."

Hathor's light. Those in the Land of Punt[101] saw
Hathor, Lady of the Horizon,[102] and her light as an
almost-setting sun fixed over their west both day
and night. Even in the heavenly Field of Reeds she
gleamed golden upon the once-deceased as here in
this existence with bones.[103]

Her radiant crown illuminated beings in all the
states of existence, all without exception. And we
saw not just humans but all the beings – plants, fish,
birds, insects, animals.

We saw the various animals and birds and fish and
plants in those states become visible; and we saw
whether they were in a happy, unhappy, low,
eminent, or intermediate position. All could be seen
from this light.[104]

---

[101] A kingdom on or around the Horn of Africa (present-day
Eritrea, Djibouti, Somalia, Ethiopia, or northeastern Sudan)
and possibly the Southern Arabian Peninsula (present-day
Yemen and Saudi Arabia). The ancient Egyptians sent
diplomatic-trading expeditions to Punt, returning with gold,
ivory, ebony, incense, animal skins, live animals, incense such
as frankincense and myrrh, as well as copper, bitumen.
[102] See the *Coffin Texts* (e.g. spell 276) for this epithet.
[103] See Skjærvø's translation of Yasht 13 ("Hymn to the
Guardian Angels") in the Zoroastrian religious text collection
the Khordeh Avesta (little Avesta) for the phrase "in the
existence with bones" in the context of describing the
Zoroastrian messiah Zarathusra's birth.
[104] See *Lotus Sutra*.

Lightland was filled with her presence. Yet evil still befell many who cried and died while she shined.[105] We saw this earth on every side replete with suffering beings.

We saw in many fields the servants of Hathor and other gods whipping and goading cows and sheep.

We saw in many marshes fowlers restraining birds by their necks so they could be offered.

We saw horses impaled by spears and arrows in battle. We saw hippopotami breaking their own legs trying to get free from their tethering.[106] And we saw in the luster of this light millions of these and other beings fattened and killed for sacrifices.

We saw the daughters and sons of the pharaoh's body attending to Hathor's golden images while snorting and screaming cows cried out and fell heavily to the ground–being hobbled, wrestled, and stabbed. We saw the blood flow from these necks and illuminate the fields and the temple floors. It flowed even into the Nile. We saw tongues hanging out and eyes rolling back from the dying.

---

[105] The *Lamentations of Isis and Nepthys* has Isis say of her murdered husband/brother Osiris: "As you rise for us you light the Two Lands, Lightland is filled with your presence; Gods and men look to you, No evil befalls them when you shine."
[106] As found at Hierakonpolis.

We saw cows and donkeys hauling coffins and stones. They even carry turquoise for Hathor's temples and priestesses. In all directions of space are beings, like sand of the desert, dishonored by humans.[107]

We saw cow heads and legs offered to the pharaoh, to Hathor, and the other gods. Some of these legs were sawed off living calves while their mothers were forced to watch and cry out in horror. And with these the bodies of birds were choked forward by hands around their necks. They hung now sullenly.

We saw thousands more cow heads placed around Nubian tombs.

We saw millions of ibises and cats sacrificed, mummified, and sold as offerings to Thoth and Bastet. All of these cried out and struggled when they realized they were in danger. They wanted to keep living.

---

[107] See *Lotus Sutra*.

*Hathor column-head from the temple of the cat-goddess Bastet
in the ancient city Bubasis*

We saw dripping newborn calves tied away from
their wide-eyed lunging mothers, whose milk would
be taken. Their wretched cries were incessant; so
they were beaten, suffering pain on pain.[108]

Hathor quaked with terror.[109]

Though we and even the gods strained to look
directly at her, amidst the degradation of
creatures,[110] the flowers and plants across all of
Egypt slowly turned towards her overflowing
emanation. These included sycamore and fig trees,
barley, emmer wheat, acacia, canary grass, darnel,
mayweed, vetchling, bulrush, nutgrass, spikerush,
mustard, dock, vetch, grapevines, lotuses, crocuses,
carob trees, thyme, acacia trees, poplar, papyrus
reeds, tamarisk, thistles, as well as the moss,
mushrooms, algae, poppies, chamomile, lilies, water
ferns, clovers, duckweeds, sedges, cereal grasses,
sorghum, and onions.

---

[108] See *Lotus Sutra*.
[109] See the *Papyrus of Mes-em-neter, Book of the Dead,
Chapter of Driving Back the Serpent Rerek in the Underworld.*
[110] See *Lotus Sutra*, chapter 2.

*Baboons worshiping the morning sun (Khepri, Ra's aspect as the
morning sun, in scarab-beetle form); Inspired by the common actual
behavior of baboons raising their hands towards the sun at dawn;
Circa 400-200 BCE.*

Baboons turned towards her and raised their palms
toward the rays sent forth above her head.

People held lotus flowers to their noses to perfume
the stench of the cowpen and the rotting flesh we
smelled across all the nomes of Egypt.

We heard the roar of all the rattling sistra across
these lands. It was an echoing layered river of
shaking. And while the light shone from her crown,
the other beings in all the directions of space

appeared to us in their own bodies and raised their voices, crying.[111]

And all the classes of the audience, priestesses and priests, numerous gods and goddesses, farmers and millers, generals and musicians, humans and beings not human, on seeing the magnificence of this great light of Hathor, were struck with astonishment and fear.

I then said unto Her Majesty, "Speak, O most eminent of goddesses! in this assembly there are thousands of beings trustful, affectionate, and respectful towards you; they will understand the words you expound."[112]

Hathor spoke:

> You say that I am your goddess of the purest
> motherly love. Listen as I show you the
> child as attacker, the sibling as enemy,
> humans murdering their mother; stealing,
> torturing, and murdering her children.[113]

> Truly–all the animals, their hearts weep.
> And the cattle lament their condition in the

---

[111] See *Lotus Sutra*, Chapter 2.
[112] See *Lotus Sutra*, Chapter 2.
[113] See the *Prophecy of Neferti*.

land of Egypt. What are these things which have come to pass? I can cry only "Destruction!"

All joy is lacking to my heart; I am totally undone. How evil is our plight through the misery of our time.[114]

Every praising mouth is filled with 'we love you' yet the words are followed by one arm raised with a goad or a whip and another with a knife.

Upon the very roads that led you here, you followed the ruts of countless carts pulled by my brethren under your whips and yokes. You used canals that we died digging. You saw us loaded onto boats and ferried to slaughter elsewhere in Egypt. You swatted the flies that investigated as you passed through their homelands. You ate and drank grains and flour sown in fields we plowed. Our tears and blood stain these paths and your bowels.

---

[114] See the Twelfth Dynasty (c. 1991 – 1803 BCE) *Admonitions of Ipuwer* (aka *Lamentations of Ipuwer*).

Tilapia fish pendant circa 1390 – 1295 BCE

To the non-humans and their Ba-souls

To the gathered cows and non-human beings, she asked:

> What have we done, that the humans have beaten us these many times?[115] Why are we in sorrow and helplessness?[116]
>
> Our happiness is all gone, the cows of the land are doleful and laid waste. Our labors, bruises, and their grain-measures are great.[117] And so it is for the Tilapia and Medjed[118] fish who delight in the Nile yet are confined in your artificial ponds. And for the bees that fly, build, and feed themselves but are robbed by your thieves. These were created from the tears of Ra. But listen now to the hum as their many souls cry out to him instead![119] And so it is for the birds, monkeys, plants, insects, and every other form of beings.

---

[115] See Balaam's Ass, *Book of Numbers*, Chapter 22.
[116] See Rameses III's description of conquered Meshwesh Libyans. Edgerton & Wilson, p. 81.
[117] See the *Prophecy of Neferti*.
[118] Worshiped at Oxyrhynchus.
[119] See *Book of Gates*, Eighth Division, #1, in the Circle of Sesheta.

Though you worship me and the Apis and other sacred bulls, and many goddesses and gods with likenesses of other forms of beings, we know how ruined we are. Our destruction is our fact.

All, look now upon me, the mistress of grief![120]

Today we will make our complaints before all!

To the Egyptian gods and goddesses

To Isis, mistress of life, ruler of fate and destiny – "Listen well, for you will continue my duties as I carry forth those of our bovine sister-goddess Bat, goddess of the feminine Ba souls. I call to you, weeping to the height of heaven! But you do not hear my voice."[121]

To her Far-Striding father Ra, she asked, "What have I done to you, that you have allowed the humans' treatment of us and done nothing? I call to

---

[120] See the *Prophecy of Neferti.*

[121] In the *Lamentations of Isis and Nepthys* (Papyrus Berlin 3008), Isis calls out to her murdered husband/brother Osiris: "While I can see I call to you, weeping to the height of heaven! But you do not hear my voice, though I am your sister whom you loved on earth, you loved none but me, the sister, the sister!"

you, weeping to the height of heaven! But you do not hear my voice. Your Ba is in the Mnevis bull. Do you feel the grief of his body? Do you know the sickness of his Ka?"[122]

To her son Horus of the Horizon,[123] she asked, "Though you see all, why do you ignore me and your aunts and uncles and cousins and our brethren? I call to you, weeping to the height of heaven! But you do not hear my voice."

To Ma'at, goddess of truth and order, weigher of hearts, whose 42 Assessors also judge the dead—"You will weigh their hearts when they are dead? What about while they live? If you will not stop them now I see no reason to bring you the dead. I call to you, weeping to the height of heaven! But you do not hear my voice."

---

[122] Concepts of the body and soul in ancient Egypt include several distinct yet combining entities that form humans before birth, throughout this life, and into the next. The Ba is the individual's personality or self. The Ka may be considered the person's individual life-force or spirit. In the afterlife, one's Ba must reunite with the Ka. The ancient Egyptian Bull hieroglyph – □ – is pronounced Ka. Sometimes it was combined with the "arm with stick of authority" hieroglyph. The pharaoh is described in terms signifying strong bull and even bull (mate) of His mother. Other parts of the combined human body and soul included the physical body, heart, shadow, name, spiritual body.

[123] Horus of the Horizon (Horemakhet) is Horus in his dawning and early morning solar form.

To Nut, at Whose Feet Is Eternity – "You protect against unclean food in the underworld. What about now? Do you know what is unclean? Harming and killing another. Make them like this now. I call to you, weeping to the height of heaven! But you do not hear my voice."

To Osiris, the Weary-Hearted – "I call to you, weeping to the height of heaven! But you do not hear my voice. Why do you not hear our lamentations?"[124]

To Ptah, the Master of Justice – "Your ba is in the Apis bull. Do you feel the grief of his body? Do you know the sickness of his ka?"

To Montu – "Your ba is in the Buchis bull. Do you feel the grief of his body? Do you know the sickness of his ba?"

To the other gods, she asked, "What have we done to you, that you have witnessed the humans' treatment of us and yet done nothing? I call to you, weeping to the height of heaven! But you do not hear my voice."

---

[124] See *The Song of the Harper*, in which the author urges the reader to enjoy life and be happy since Osiris doesn't hear one's lamentations or spare one from death due to their travails.

Tribute from Nubia presented to Pharaoh Tutankhamun in the tomb of the Egyptian Viceroy of Kush, Huy (circa 1353–1327 BCE). Note the cow-skin leather on the men in the upper left, the ox-cart in the upper center, the cow-skin shields in the upper right, and the Hathor-associated Menat necklace held by the woman in the lower left.

Shabti of the Adoratrice of Hathor ("Duahathor") Henettawy, wife of Pinedjem I. Third Intermediate Period ca. 1064–1055 B.C.

Outer coffin of queen Duathathor Henuttawy, the Adoratrice of Hathor, wife of Pinedjem I. Third Intermediate Period ca. 1064–1055 B.C.

*Cleopatra VII Thea Philopator (father-loving goddess), final pharaoh
(51 - 30 BCE) of the Ptolemaic Kingdom making offerings to Isis. She
also portrays herself as Isis or Hathor in other imagery, including at
the temples of Dendera, Edfu, and Kom Ombo.*

To the pharaoh, royal wives, and their children

To the pharaoh, she said:

> Pharaoh, mighty bull of your mother – I
> nursed you as a child. I will lead you into
> the afterlife. You were to maintain order and
> Ma'at.[125]
>
> Is this the kind of order you think we want?
> You will never know peace in the Field of
> Reeds while you and your descendants treat
> us and the laborers and enslaved peoples
> like this.
>
> You live on your fathers and feed on your
> mothers and children. You eat their entrails.
> You lasso, bind, cut their throats, carve them
> up, and cook meals of them in your
> dinner-pots. You eat their big ones for your
> morning meal, their middle ones for your
> evening meal, and their little ones for your
> night meal. You make burnt offerings of
> their oldest males and females for your fuel.
> Your kettles and mouths are filled with

---

[125] Ma'at encompasses truth, balance, order, harmony, law,
morality, and justice. The pharaoh's primary responsibility
was to maintain Ma'at.

thighs and forelegs. You take the shadows from their owners.[126]

You have all the power in your world and this is what you choose. Your scribes write of the Heavenly Cow and the mayhem and death she brought upon humanity when Ra turned me into Sekhmet for his vengeance[127] – yet who is writing of the needs of the Earthly cow?

Your mothers, sisters, and daughters dress up like me. If you see your mother and wife as Hathor, why do you make us and your bovine brothers and sisters suffer!

You herd cows around your temples only to kill and profit by them. Their legs are hobbled so you can wrestle them to the ground, ensnared before my image. Their throats and nostrils are stopped up,

---

[126] See the "Cannibal Hymn" of the *Pyramid Texts of Unas*, Utterances 273 - 274. Lichtheim 1973, pp. 36 - 38.
[127] The Middle Kingdom (c. 2100 – 1700 BCE) Book of the Heavenly Cow contains the myth of Ra inflicting divine punishment on humanity by having Hathor turn into the lion goddess Sekhmet and almost completely annihilating humanity before he tricked her to get so drunk that she passed out and stopped killing the humans. When she awoke, she returned to her gentle form of Hathor.

destroyed.[128] You offer their heads and forelegs to the gods. Our castrated sons are goaded to carry your bodies to your tombs before being slaughtered and laid alongside you.

Isis goes before your coffin. Her sister Nephthys follows behind you. They grieve for you, but who wails for these cows trodding westward to their unjustified slaughters?

---

[128] See Ramses III's description of conquered Meshwesh Libyan peoples. Edgerton & Wilson, p. 81.

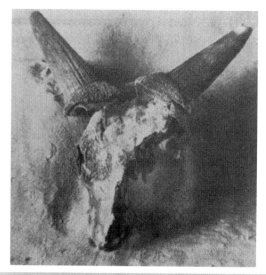

Skull of Buchis Bull "M" (top) and Buchis Bull "13" (bottom)

Skeleton of a mummified Buchis Bull

Mummified head of an Apis bull

You bury the cows and dogs from your daughters' palatial sanctuaries in their own graves–as you do with the bodies of the sacred Apis, Buchis, and Mnevis bulls and their parents.[129] On the day of the burial of the mother of the Apis bull, you and others bring petitional offerings attempting to bribe the ka soul of this cow to provide you with children and other good things.[130] What

---

[129] See the Maru-Aten palace of Meriaten, daughter of pharaoh Akhenaten.
[130] See "Letters to gods" by Edward O. D. Love.

benefits are due to the non-Apis children she bore? You bury as well the sacred cows of Hesat. Why do you ignore the rest of these and other animals?

You ask me to protect your graves in the cobra form of Meretseger, she who loves silence–What do your workers do with the snakes they disturb while digging and adorning these graves? Where is the silence amongst the cries of the slaughtered and fearful?

You hunt my children after your riders herd them into pens, hemmed in and terror-stricken. Then you lay death upon them with arrows and knives, thinking yourself powerful. You boast of this powerful achievement on inscribed scarabs sent throughout Egypt and to foreign kings and queens.[131]

---

[131] Amenhotep III did this to spread word of his power and wealth.

Silver-plated bull Rhyton ceremonial drinking vessel. The Hittite king Tushratta sent gold-plated ivory bull Rhytons to pharaoh Akhenaten as part of the wedding gifts he sent with his daughter to join the Egyptian pharaoh. The Hittites used the Rhyton in some of their animal sacrifices, having the shepherd of the animals being slaughtered call for the deity to kill them and their family if they substituted a weaker animal for the intended fattened one.

Hathor continued:

> And you send horses and goats to these foreigners–why do you do this? They do not want to walk to Karduniaš.[132] Like the Maryannu families of human

---

[132] See for example Amarna Letters of 1350 - 1335 BCE in which Amenḥotep III and Kadašman-Enlil, the Kassite dynasty king of Babylon (aka Karduniaš during the Middle Assyrian and Neo-Assyrian times), hope that the others' horses are doing well, yet exchange horses with each other as gifts. They also discuss and negotiate the sending of a Mittanian daughter as a gift.

chariot-warriors, are the children of the
bodies of Egyptian horses at the head of the
Hittite cavalry and those of the bodies of
theirs at the head of yours when you battle?
Do your archers kill your own horses?

Hittite cavalry crushing an enemy

Was the mare in heat who Muwatalli II sent
out to disrupt your chariot-horses a mother
of Egyptian blood? Do not send your horses
to die and become captive amongst the sons
of the Nine Bows.

Let these horses live here in Egypt where
they are born. How many of them die en
route to your peers? Let them die here in
Egypt in peace where they are born.

But let them die after comfortable lives, not
through siege and starvation. Do not
admonish your enemies whose horses die
when you besiege them![133]

You rule over a world enclosed within a
desire for flesh. You make terror in us[134]
– all creatures are bewildered, suffer, and
die.[135]

The pharaoh loudly declared:

Hail to you, Hathor, Lady of the Two Lands,
who gives life and dominion![136]

I dispatched inspectors and overseers to the
turquoise desert of my mother, the goddess
Hathor, the lady of the turquoise! They
carried to you silver, gold, byssus, fine linen,
and many things as numerous as the
sand-grains, and laid them before you. The
like had never been seen before—since
kings began to reign…

---

[133] Piye did this.
[134] As the pharaohs aimed to do in their enemies. See Edgerton
& Wilson, p. 6 from the records of Ramses III's war against
the Nubians.
[135] See *Bhagavad Gita*.
[136] See inscription from tomb of Amenhotep III.

Hathor interrupted:

Cease your boasting!

Heretofore, pharaohs are not needed to bring order to the world or treasure to temples, but to dominate and degrade them both.

In your temples you show images of horses and oxen and mules and cows in battle and war trains. Look into the eyes of these images and think of their pains, not your own riches and glories! How did you become powerful, grow, and protect your strength?

Seth of the bodies of Nut and Geb will bury your temples through the thousands of years. We suffer now.

If you are the king of Egypt, you are the king not just of Egypt's peoples, but also of the animals and fields and the Nile and other rivers. You must protect all creatures and the land and water itself so they may be healthy in your time and your grandchildren's times.

Appoint Overseers of the Welfare of Animals. Instruct the Overseers of Cattle and your Generals in righteous acts towards animals. This too is part of Ma'at.

Inculcate these in your people, the so-called cattle of the gods. Promote compassion, gentleness, and goodness.[137] No task is more important to you than promoting the well-being of all living beings. Thus you will make them happy in this world and help yourself reach the Field of Reeds in the next.[138] But even if it did not help you gain eternal life, it is worth doing for their peace alone in this life.

You have seen the sufferings in every land and field and lake and river in these lands. But the one who is the master of the lands looks on and does nothing to prevent it; no, the master expands the sufferings rather than protecting the fearful.[139]

You seek glory by smashing the heads of your enemies and seizing or destroying tens of thousands of their cattle, donkeys, goats, sheep, women, men, and children. More and

---

[137] See *Edicts of Ashoka*, Pillar Edict VII.
[138] See *Edicts of Ashoka*, Rock Edict VI.
[139] See the *Cycle of Songs in Honor of Senwosret III* for the praise of the pharaoh for being "a resting place which protects the fearful man from his enemy."

truer glory is gained through peace. For what you need, trade may be founded on mutual respect and good will. Thus will your people thrive and your neighbors love you. Those like Userkaf and Hatshepsut who make expeditions to Punt gain greater glory than those who massacre Nubians, Asiatics, and Libyans. Trade via ships to Punt, Gubla,[140] and elsewhere lets Shu's breath carry the weight, rather than breaking the backs of animals or humans.

Yet do not suppress conquered peoples' sacred rites, though you find them objectionable. Eradicating culture and languages to eradicate suffering is unacceptable.

Glory is only of value in so far as the people, at present and in the future, live in accordance with compassion.[141] Compassion is a pharaoh's true monument.[142]

---

[140] Byblos, present-day Lebanon. A port city usually allied with Egypt, providing cedar trees in trade. Home to the goddess Baalat Gubal (Lady of Byblos), associated with and sharing imagery with Hathor.

[141] See *Edicts of Ashoka*, Rock Edict X.

[142] See the *Instructions of Ptahhotep*, written by the Vizier Ptahhotep during the Fifth Dynasty rule of Djedkare Isesi circa 2375–2350 BCE.

There is no offering you can bring to my
temple that can equal the gift of kindness to
animals and abstention from their slaughter
or sacrifice.[143] Many ceremonies are
performed in my temple. These are of
doubtful value. They may achieve their
purpose, or they may not. Moreover, the
purposes for which they are performed are
limited to this world. The ceremony of
universal kindness, on the other hand, is not
limited to time. This kindness must include
restraint of violence to living creatures.
Even if it does not achieve its object in this
world, it produces unlimited merit in the
next world. But if it produces its object in
this world, it achieves both effects: the
purpose desired in this world and unlimited
merit in the next.[144]

To the Priestesses and Priests

Now Hathor called on the priestesses and priests.
Gathered before her were those from her own
temples, as well as those of the Apis, Buchis, and
Mnevis bulls, of Hesat, of Isis, and of the other gods
and goddesses. Herdsmen of the cows of many
gods' temples were brought among these.

---

[143] See *Edicts of Ashoka*, Rock Edict XI.
[144] See *Edicts of Ashoka*, Rock Edict IX.

Isis (left) and Nepthys (right) as kite birds guarding the deceased official Sennedjem (13th century BCE). In addition to being a scribe and official in the community of Deir el-Medina tomb artisans, he and his wife Iyneferti bore the titles "servant of Hathor" and "singer of Hathor," respectively.

From the tomb of the official Sennedjem (13th century BCE). In addition to being a scribe and official in the community of Deir el-Medina tomb artisans, he and his wife Iyneferti bore the titles "servant of Hathor" and "singer of Hathor," respectively.

From the tomb of the official Sennedjem

Those of Hathor

To her priestesses and priests, she said:

> You hang an ankh round my neck and a bell
> on my childrens'. Oh that I could remove it
> to end this life and end my suffering. And if
> I could remove the bell from my childrens'
> necks you would not be able to follow and
> harass them. You should know that the bell
> ringing hurts their ears.[145] As does your
> incessant sistra rattling. Let me give birth to

---

[145] See Johns J, Patt A, Hillmann E. *"Do bells affect behaviour and heart rate variability in grazing dairy cows?"*, 2015.

no more daughters and sons to carry forth
their inheritance of pain. I am ready to die.

By you, our false protectors, our flesh is
hacked up to the duration of eternity.[146]

Hathor's priestesses and priests exclaimed, holding
their arms bent forward with palms towards the sky:

> Hail to you, Hathor, Lady of the Sycamore,
> Mistress of the Sky and Bigeh, Lady of
> Love, you who give life to all living things.
> Do not lament! We praise and honor you, oh
> great one. We prepare offerings of cattle,
> birds, milk, honeyed bread, and cakes for
> you. We bring you dancers and musicians.
> We maintain your temples. We dress your
> statue.

---

[146] See Ramses III's depiction of the conquered Sea Peoples:
"Hacked up is their flesh to the duration of eternity." Edgerton
& Wilson, p. 39.

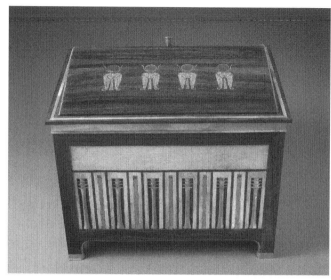

Chest of Sithathoriunet (her name means "daughter of Hathor of Dendera"). She was a daughter of Pharaoh Senuseret II, who reigned 1897 - 1878 BCE.

Statue of Djedher, a priest of Horus and Hathor and royal chamberlain (circa 200 - 150 BCE)

With a steady gaze, Hathor replied:

> Yes, you possess and slay the sacred cattle
> and pity them not, that you may hold
> yourselves not guilty. And you say, "Hathor
> is great, for I am rich." And you tell the
> people, "Bring offerings for Hathor and the
> priests, that she will bring you riches too."
> You lease the cows of the temples to work in
> your fields. And again you say, "Hathor is
> great, for I am rich." And when the cows of
> the fields' backs are broken and they die of
> disease and exhaustion, you are not pitiful to
> the cows or vexed toward the lessor, but
> require only restitution and accounting
> through payments of fine linen and return of
> the cows' skins.

Gathering honey. From the tomb of Rekhmire (1479 - 1425 BCE).
Drawn by Nina M. Davies (1881–1965)

Hathor continued:

> This bread you offer is made of blood. How
> did you get this honey? Did you yourselves
> suck it from flowers and brew it in your own
> bellies? Or did you steal it from the bees and
> disrupt their cities and cause some to die?
> No, you don't even rob the bees yourselves,
> but tax the honeyworkers.
>
> They stun, starve, and disturb these bees to
> style your wigs and corpses! Did you first
> slay one of my calves so that the bees would
> rise through its horns in your Bugonia
> ritual?
>
> How do you mix and congeal your
> perfumes? With animal fat!

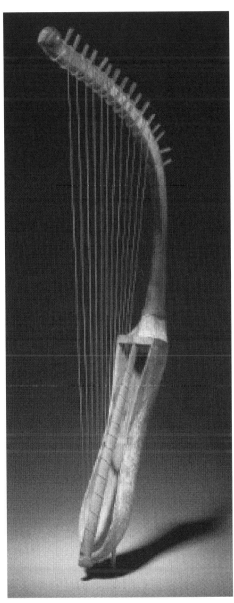

Ancient Egyptian harp (sacred to Hathor) strung with sinew (animal tendons)

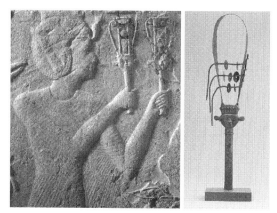

Sistrum rattles, sacred to Hathor; Played also by her son mythological son Ihy (fathered by her other son, Horus)

Ivory Hathor-headed clappers. New Kingdom.

And what instruments do these musicians play? A harp with the sinew and gut of my brethren! A tambourine and tam-tam drum with our skin! Ivory clappers with my face carved into the severed tusks of murdered elephants? Fools! How many had to suffer for you to offer your praises? You have misunderstood what it is to cherish and love and celebrate.

Make no more music with such morbid instruments.

Even the dancers wear skirts made from the skins of my brethren.[147]

And how many among you priestesses and priests own land on which this blood spills?

You sell even our feces while destroying our bodies and seizing our calves.

The myrrh that you burn comes from repeatedly wounding trees to produce its healing resin.

---

[147] See Solange Ashby - Sacred Dancers: Nubian Women as Priestesses of Hathor.

Do not sing my praises while defiling my brethren lest your heads fall off!

Amos said:

Though you offer her burnt offerings and your meat offerings, she will not accept them.

Take away from her the noise of your songs; for she will not hear the melodies of your harps, voices, drums, and sistra.[148]

Micah said:

No, she will not be pleased with thousands of offered calves, geese, ducks, and cakes, or with ten thousands of rivers of oil. Oh humans, what is good, and what anyone asks of you, is but to do justly, and to love mercy,

---

[148] See *Amos* 5:20-24, "Surely the day of the LORD shall be not light, but darkness, blackest night without a glimmer. I loathe, I spurn your festivals, I am not appeased by your solemn assemblies. If you offer Me burnt offerings—or your meal offerings—I will not accept them; I will pay no heed to your gifts of fatlings. Spare Me the sound of your hymns, and let Me not hear the music of your lutes. But let justice well up like water, righteousness like an unfailing stream."

and to walk humbly with your kin and
kine.[149]

Zechariah then asked the gathered humans:

> But who will feed the flocks of slaughter
> and work, even the poorest among them, yet
> slay and drive them not?[150]

A priestess of Hathor said:

> That which is held in abomination to me is
> the block of slaughter of the god.[151] That
> which is abominable, that which is
> abominable I will not eat. An abominable

---

[149] See *Micah* 6:6-9, "With what shall I approach the LORD,
do homage to God on high? Shall I approach Him with burnt
offerings, with calves a year old? Would the LORD be pleased
with thousands of rams, with myriads of streams of oil? Shall I
give my first-born for my transgression, the fruit of my body
for my sins? 'He has told you, O man, what is good, and what
the LORD requires of you: Only to do justice and to love
goodness, and to walk modestly with your god; Then will your
name achieve wisdom.'"

[150] See *Zechariah* 11:4-5, 11:7: "Thus said my God the LORD:
Tend the sheep meant for slaughter, whose buyers will
slaughter them with impunity, whose seller will say 'Praised
be the LORD! I'll get rich,' and whose shepherd will not pity
them....So I tended the sheep meant for slaughter, for those
poor men of the sheep. I got two staffs, one of which I named
Favor and the other Unity, and I proceeded to tend the sheep."

[151] Directly quoted from the Book of the Dead Papyrus of Nu,
The Chapter of Not Letting the Heart of Nu, Whose Word is
Truth, Be Carried Away From Him in Khert-Neter.

thing is filth, I will not eat thereof. That which is an abomination unto my Ka shall not enter my body. I will live upon that whereon live the gods and the Spirit-souls. I shall live, and I shall be master of their cakes. I am master of them, and I shall eat them under the trees of the dweller in the House of Hathor, my Lady, the Mistress of Iken.[152]

---

[152] Directly quoted from the *Book of the Dead Papyrus of Ani*, The Chapter of Making the Transformation Into Ptah.

Those of the Apis, Buchis, and Mnevis Bulls

To the priestesses and priests of the Apis, Buchis, and Mnevis bulls, she said:

> You say that the Apis bull is the incarnation of the Ba-soul of Ptah. And the Mnevis likewise the Ba of Ra. And the Buchis of the Ka-souls of both Ra and Montu. These bulls are said to be the indwelling images of these gods.

Hathor continued, addressing all the humans:

> We see inscriptions with dedications from pharaohs to ensure that the bulls would go to the Field of Reeds after death. And the bulls' parents.
>
> Why not the other children? Do not sacred parents give birth to sacred children? Does Khnum not craft them all, human and non-human?
>
> No, the pharaoh pays for the burial of those whose riches might be inherited. Who would bury an executed one whose riches have already been taken?

It is for the cows as it is for the humans–very few lead extravagant lives of comfort while everyone else is wretched and worked to death.

You live closely with the bulls. You know their ways and discern meaning from their movements. And yet you know they are like any other bull. And all the children of the body of the Apis and Mnevis bulls and their sacred mothers greet you with nuzzling kindness, yet you protect only one of them. Hesat[153] nurses them all! The mothers and fathers mourn for their children who are crushed in infancy–who see the face of the crocodile without ever having lived.[154] The mothers and fathers mourn their unwanted boys who are smashed against the walls, and the suckling children thrown out onto the desert.[155] So too with the mothers and

---

[153] Hesat is a goddess manifestation of Hathor, said to nurse the Mnevis bull.

[154] An expression from *The Man Who Was Weary With Life* (aka the *Dispute Between a Man and His Ba)*. Here, a man's Ba spirit tells of a peasant whose wife and children were killed by a storm. He says he grieves not for his wife who must inevitably have died, but for his children who died in infancy before ever having lived.

[155] Referencing the *Admonitions of Ipuwer,* which tells of the chaos and cruelty affecting the humans of the First Intermediate Period, when the centralized Pharaonic state was decentralized and engaged in civil war.

fathers of all the other cows that are not favored.

You could encourage better treatment of all bulls and all cows among the people. This would win you my approval and the respectful trust of their parents.

Then you will see that it is not just the bulls and cows which deserve kindness and peace.

Also the fish of Hatmehyt and the fish of themselves. And the bald ibises of Akhty and the bald ibises of themselves. And the blue herons of Atum and Bennu and the blue herons of themselves.

Let air be given unto these beings[156], not capture and suffering! Let them pass over the sky.[157]

And the cobras of Wadjet and the cobras of themselves. So too with the scarab beetles of Khepri and the scarab beetles of themselves. Do not step on them but let them go about their days.

---

[156] See Papyrus of Nu *Book of the Dead*, The Chapter of Giving Air in the Underworld.
[157] See Papyrus of Nebseni *Book of the Dead*, The Chapter of Coming Forth By Day in the Underworld.

Though you see the images of the gods
dwelling within some of their species, know
that each of these has their own lives outside
the purposes and images of the gods. They
protect themselves and their babies. From
this you know they desire to live
undisturbed. So do them no harm and let
them be.

Priests offer the severed leg of a living calf while their mother cries out (protruding tongue). From the Opening of the Mouth scene in the Book of the Dead Papyrus of Hunefer. The calf's vitality is transferred to the deceased. Hunefer was the Overseer of Royal Cattle during the reign of pharaoh Seti I. Circa 1285 BCE.

Detail of a living calf whose foreleg was severed for a dead human while their mother cries out (protruding tongue). From the Opening of the Mouth scene in the Book of the Dead Papyrus of Hunefer. The calf's vitality is transferred to the deceased. Hunefer was the Overseer of Royal Cattle during the reign of pharaoh Seti I. Circa 1285 BCE.

A living calf's foreleg is severed while their mother cries out. From the Tomb of Amenmose, High Priest of Amenhotep of the Forecourt. Early 19th Dynasty (circa 1525 - 1504 BCE).

Head of Amun's wife, Shepenupet II, daughter of King Piye (Kushite Nubian conqueror of Egypt, Pharaoh of the 25th Dynasty, mid 700's BCE), wearing Hathor's crown.[158]

Qetesh with the face, head, and headdress of Hathor. Standing on a lion, she holds lotus flowers and a snake. She is flanked by the Egyptian god Min to her right and the Ugaritic god Reseph on her left. In the lower register, the commissioner Qeh and his family are shown worshiping the goddess Anat.

---

[158] Another of Piye's daughters, Mutirdis, served as Chief Prophet of Hathor and Mut in Thebes. His daughter Tabekenamun was a Nubian queen who served as a priestess of Hathor at the temples of Hathor in Gebelein and Dendera.

Other Priestesses and Priests

The milk you pour in libations for Osiris in Nubia parches the lips of the calves who cry out for their hobbled mothers.[159] Amun has many herds, being tens of thousands, thousands, hundreds, and tens, without knowing the number of all yearling calves of their mothers.[160]

Let the people know that if they beat the cattle which they lease from the temples, they are beating the gods themselves. For, all cattle are holy; as are other creatures.

You must train priests in two kinds of medical treatment–treatments for humans and treatments for animals.[161] But do not perform reckless experiments on either to learn the efficacies of herbs and procedures. Some cite many potential benefits that might result from the knowledge gained by such study. But thus do you increase suffering while trying to reduce it. Do no harm to any being–human or non-human.

---

[159] See Calling out to Isis: Interview with Dr. Solange Ashby.
[160] *Stele of the Dream* by the last Pharaoh of the 25th Dynasty and ruler of the Kingdom of Kush, Tantamani (d. 653 BCE).
[161] See *Edicts of Ashoka*, Rock Edict II.

Gerzeh Palette (c.3500 – 3200 BCE)

Ramses III's son Khaemwaset with a Hathoric sistrophorus statue

To the Generals

Hathor now addressed the generals of the pharaoh's armies.

To the generals, she said:

> You could not wage conquering wars in distant lands without the yoked cows and suffering donkeys and mules who carry your train.
>
> You use the sinew of our guts and horns from our heads in your archers' bows. The

points on some of your spears and arrows are hafted to the wood with our dried skin wrappings. Feather fletchings guide the arrows into the flesh of bodies towards death. Thus, human blood is first touched by the remains of our slaughtered corpses. Our blood is intertwined with those of your human victims. And also within you when you are finally killed. Verily, when you appear, all life except the vultures' ceases.[162]

Let the arrowmaker be stung by gnats and bit by sand fleas. Thus he is judged.[163]

You force horses of unknown number to die before you in your charges. Soldiers slip and fall prostrate in the blood of the horses[164] and their fellow humans on either side. They lie in heaps on the desolate land amongst the woeful writing horses, whose lifetimes and

---

[162] See Ramses III's celebration of victory over the Libyans, where his officials and companions say "Thou art Re, as thou risest on Egypt. When thou appearest, mankind lives." Edgerton & Wilson, p. 13.

[163] See the discussion of the arrowmaker in the Middle Kingdom literary text, *The Satire on the Trades*.

[164] See Ramses III's account in Papyrus Harris I of battle with the Nubians, in which "He looks upon bowmen as women; making the land of Kush into something nonexistent, prostrate in their blood before his horses." See Edgerton & Wilson, p. 1.

souls are finished.[165] The horses flip and
fall–their necks and legs break. They bleed
from their necks and chests, pierced by
spears and arrows. Swords slash their
shrieking faces. Some cry and writhe for
hours after the battle completes. All these
horses' feet have ceased to tread Egypt
forever.[166] They will never again see their
families or drink from the Nile.

You plunder cattle and enslave defeated
people after your battles. And you brand us
all with fire. If you did not first abuse us,
you could not extend your bloody hand on
people far away. The root of your violence
to humans is violence to us. So it has been
since the times of your ancestral
cattle-raiders.

And with their cattle, you carry off your
enemies' women and sons. You cut down

---

[165] See Ramses III's account in Papyrus Harris I of battle with
the Libyans, in which "the Temeh, slain their places in heaps
before his horses, causing them to cease boasting in their
land." And of the Libyans, "their lifetime and their soul are
finished." Edgerton & Wilson, pp. 11-12.
[166] See Ramses III's celebration of victory over the Libyans
where he says that the Sped and Meshwesh tribes "have
ceased to tread Egypt forever." Edgerton & Wilson, p. 13.

their grain and set fire to their fields.[167] And this you say is justice?

With the cows, donkeys and horses, the soldiers are brought to your camps when they are still children.

Beatings are given to all of their bodies–human and non-human alike. Their heads are split open with wounds. They are laid down and beaten like papyrus. They are struck with torments.

Together they carry rations and water upon their shoulders and backs. The vertebrae of their backs are broken, while they drink foul water. Those who return from war are like a stick which the worm has devoured. They are sick, prostration overtakes them.[168]

And who wails and laments when you send their kin to die – yes, the women whose beneficence you seek from me. Provide it yourselves by abstaining from needless

[167] See the *Semna Stela* placed on the border with Nubia by Senwosret III.
[168] See *The Hardships of the Soldier's Life (Papyrus Anastasi IV, 9, 4-10,1)* in which the treatment of soldiers is compared to that of donkeys and plucked birds. The author is refuting another scribe's assertion that the life of a soldier is better than that of a scribe.

violence on all beings! So too could you relieve the mothers and fathers of the cows you torment and kill.

At least you feed the vultures!

The Overseer of All the Horses of His Majesty said:

Oh Hathor, mistress of Cusae[169] – we who have experienced war wish most of all to see it extinct. But if we release the horses who pull our chariots, we will be vulnerable to invaders from other lands. So too with the oxen, donkeys, and mules. Not all will be as enlightened as you bid us. They will storm upon our lands if we diminish our strength and our reach. These depend on movement and transport. If we loosed our animals we would deliver many hosts upon our brethren. There is no Ma'at without war. Our enemies would seize these herds and grow richer and fatter.

Hathor was silent. How could she reply to this general? The points he made were valid – if the Egyptians were completely non-violent and forsook

---

[169] See tomb inscription of Djehuty. Cusae was in the 14th Nome of Ancient Egypt, known as the Lower Sycamore and Viper nome. Hathor is the Mistress of the Sycamore.

the chariot and wagon-train, they would be conquered from all sides. Yet, she abhorred the violence done to animals, people, and the creatures of the land who were destroyed by human war.

She asked Kamadhenu and the priestesses and priests of the goddesses and gods of other lands for their thoughts.

The priestesses and priests of the Sacred Ox of Pythagoras told how the ox and the Pythagoreans were indeed slain in such ways. Pythagoras himself could not escape–he refused to trample over a field of sacred fava beans that lay in his path to safety.

Kamadhenu of India told Hathor that the kings, ministers, deities, and philosophers of her lands had reckoned with this question.

Hathor and Kamadhenu conferred and then spoke:

> Reduce the amount of violence to the bare minimum. And ever strive to reduce that minimum.

Do not seek to extend your realms or
trespass against your neighbors to take
anything from them.[170]

Build defensive fortresses and guard-posts.
Fortify your borders and your buffer
zones.[171]

Let war be only a means of restoring peace
and maintaining order; not as a means of
enrichment or glory. Despicable is one who
forcefully binds the land to themself.[172] Do
not wrong your neighbor; thus they will
have nothing to avenge. Fight only in
defense. And do not provoke your opponent
to attack first only so you may strike back.

Use diplomacy rather than arms. Establish
treaties and renew existing ones in order not
to permit hostility to occur between you and
your neighbors forever.[173] It is expedient to
work for the future.[174] Form marriage
alliances. Send food when your neighbors

---

[170] See the c. 1259 BCE Treaty Between the Hittites and
Egyptians.
[171] See the Egyptian Middle Kingdom text (circa 2025 – 1700
BCE), *The Teaching For King Merikare*.
[172] See again *The Teaching for King Merikare*.
[173] See the c. 1259 BCE Treaty Between the Hittites and
Egyptians.
[174] See again *The Teaching for King Merikare*.

have famine and allow nomads onto your lands. Reduce taxes on your people during times of hardship to prevent unrest.

Do not accumulate wealth as this must be done by force. If you have no treasures, none will seek to seize them from you.

Understand why they come armed to your lands – are they fleeing another force, are they seeking glory, are they striving to avenge a wrong (perceived or actual)? Based on this knowledge, the truly magnanimous find ways to address others' concerns rather than only thinking about those of one's own kingdom.

Having first tried all peaceful means, there will be times of war in defense of your kingdom and its peoples, animals, and fields.

In these cases, justice and order dictate restraint and an eye towards peace, not vengeance or conquest.

If your opponents strike with spears do not strike back with chariots.[175] Subdue but do

---

[175] See *Mahabarata*.

not annihilate your opponent. Let them save face with their own people and raise their own children in life.

Treat captive humans and animals like your own children.

Heal their wounded combatants, animals, and citizens.

Do not seize them or their animals. No, release them when things are settled. For if you enslave them, they will be justified in whatever means necessary to secure their freedom and return to their own peoples, lands, rivers, and seas.

Do not burn their fields or poison their wells to starve their people and animals. Provide them with food and supplies for their safe return home.

Let the animals who bore your train or led your charges retire to grazing after battles.[176]

---

[176] See the ancient Sanskrit treatise *Arthashastra* (circa 3rd century BCE – 2nd century CE), Book II, Chapter XXX. "Stallions which are incapacitated owing to old age, disease or hardships of war, and, being therefore rendered unfit for use in war live only to consume food shall in the interests of citizens and country people be allowed to cross steeds."

And give your attention to the chariot donkeys and to the men as well.[177] Let your soldiers rest so their hearts do not harden. For, if they dwell too long in violence, they will bring it home with them when they return to farming.

By following these precepts you will secure a prosperous peace for your people, for your animals, for your fields, for your children, and for your neighbors. When war inevitably arises, you will minimize its harms and know the way back to peace. And by treating your opponent well when war is concluded, you will delay its resurgence.

In your tombs and temples, memorialize in carvings your actions of peace-making and benevolence rather than violence and subduing. For thus will you instruct your children and be judged for now and forever.

---

[177] See Papyrus British Museum 10326: "And give your attention to the chariot donkeys and to the men who are in the field as well."

15.—Wall E. Upper register, Kyky and his wife before the gates of the Nether World.
Lower register, Kyky counting the cattle of the temples of the gods.

Pl. XV

From the tomb of the Chief Accountant of the Cattle of Amun, Kyky.

From the tomb of the Chief Accountant of the Cattle of Amun, Kyky.

From the tomb of the Chief Accountant of the Cattle of Amun, Kyky. He and his wife before a Hathor-headed object.

From the tomb of the Chief Accountant of the Cattle of Amun, Kyky. Note the four cows before him.

A woman with captured birds and lotus flowers. From the tomb of Menna, a high-ranking official under pharaoh Amenhotep III (titles include: 'Overseer of Fields of Amun', 'Overseer of Plowlands of Amun', 'Overseer of Fields of the Lord of the Two Lands', 'Scribe of the Fields of the Lord of the Two Lands of South and North', 'Scribe of the Lord of the Two Lands'), circa 1422-1411 BCE.

To the Overseer of the Treasury and Overseer and Counters of the Cattle

To the Overseer and Counters of the Cattle, Hathor said:

> Everywhere you have us hit by clods or weapons. Our backs are broken–laden down under vessels filled with grain.[178] We yell and pull; you strike us again when we bellow in pain. Everywhere we are threatened with sticks, and our bodies are emaciated from hunger and thirst.[179] Everywhere you scorch our flesh with possessive seals. And for our service, you destroy us when we cease to be of use to you.

The Overseer of Cattle replied, "But Hathor, Chieftaness of the Desert Cemeteries![180] You ask us to do something against nature. Look at the lion and the hawk and the crocodile who live on flesh. Should we feed lame cattle when we cannot fully feed the people?"

---

[178] A condition which the author of the *Admonitions of Ipuwer* laments having befallen the formerly wealthy during the First Intermediate Period after the decentralization and civil war of the Egyptian state.
[179] See *Lotus Sutra*.
[180] See offering text of Kheruef.

Hathor replied:

Yes, some others live on flesh. But not like
you humans. You do not need flesh, milk, or
blood as a diet to survive. And the ways
these animals hunt are far removed from
your organized pens and cages of
harvesting. You who live now, what
madness, what frenzy drives you to the
pollution of shedding blood, you who have
such a superfluity of necessities? Why
slander the earth by implying that she cannot
support you? Why impiously offend
crop-giving Geb as if you did not receive
enough from his hands?[181] Are you not
ashamed to mingle domestic crops with
blood and gore?

No, for the sake of a little flesh you deprive
them of sun, of light, of the duration of life
to which they are entitled by birth and being.
Then you go on to assume that when they
utter cries and squeaks their speech is
inarticulate; that they do not, begging for
mercy, entreating, seek justice.

---

[181] See Plutarch (c. 46 – 119 CE), *On the Eating of Flesh*, I,
994 A-B

Let the people know that if they beat the cattle which they lease from the pharaoh or the temples, they are beating the gods themselves. For all cattle are holy; as are all other creatures.

Humans and cows work to provide sacrifices, including the cows' bodies and lives. From the Theban tomb chapel of Nakht, a scribe and astronomer during the reign of pharaoh Thutmose IV, circa 1410 – 1370 BCE.

Tomb of Nakht under Tuthmosis IV (1420 – 1411 BCE)

Tomb of Nebseny under Tuthmosis IV (1420 – 1411 BCE)

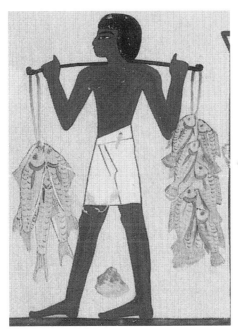

From the Tomb of Nakht under Tuthmosis IV (1420 – 1411 BCE)

Tomb of Nebamun (a scribe and grain counter at a temple at Thebes in the mid-14th century BCE). Note the cat biting a bird in front of him.

From the tomb of Nebamun

From the tomb of Nebamun

To the Farmers, Fishers, and Fowlers

To the farmers, she said:

> You beat us to plow your fields as the
> foremen beat you.

> The administrators beat you vigorously,
> demand the grain when there is none, bind
> your wife and children.[182]

> And the priests and priestesses stockpile

> and waste your harvest in empty offerings.
> They tax you to fill their temples with gold
> and statues and offerings!

> They trade these goods and make
> themselves rich!

> And yet they also charge you to lease their
> fields and cattle!

> With these riches they purchase higher titles
> and honors.[183] They dedicate a stela or relief
> in order to appease the people and appear
> pious to the gods.

---

[182] See the *Reminder of the Scribe's Superior Status (Papyrus Sallier I, 6, 1-9).*

[183] See e.g. *Tebtuni Papyri,* vol I.

I hear the field hands cry out forever! Your voices are louder than the ravens'. Your fingers have become ulcerous.[184] We are both always in another's service–feeble, and subject to many diseases as we go about in the world unprotected.[185]

You are under the yoke of the plow with us! Neither of us have even one day of rest in seven.[186] Don't you see!

We step on the seeds and thresh the grain but are denied the ears of the crops.

You have plowed wickedness, you have reaped iniquity. Sow in righteousness, reap

---

[184] See the discussion of the farmer/field-hand in the Middle Kingdom literary text, *The Satire on the Trades.*

[185] See *Lotus Sutra.*

[186] See *Deuteronomy* 5:12-15, "Observe the sabbath day and keep it holy, as the LORD your God has commanded you. Six days you shall labor and do all your work, but the seventh day is a sabbath of the LORD your God; you shall not do any work—you, your son or your daughter, your male or female slave, or any of your cattle, or the stranger in your settlements, so that your male and female slave may rest as you do. Remember that you were a slave in the land of Egypt and that the LORD your God freed you from there with a mighty hand and an outstretched arm; therefore the LORD your God has commanded you to observe the sabbath day."

in mercy.[187] Take off the yoke on our
jaws![188]

To the fowlers, Hathor said:[189]

---

[187] See *Hosea* 10:10-13, "'When I chose them, I broke them in,
harnessing them for two furrows. Ephraim became a trained
heifer, but preferred to thresh; I placed a yoke upon her sleek
neck. I will make Ephraim do advance plowing; Judah shall do
main plowing! Jacob shall do final plowing! Sow
righteousness for yourselves; reap the fruits of goodness;
break for yourselves betimes fresh ground of seeking the
LORD, so that you may obtain a teacher of righteousness.'
You have plowed wickedness, you have reaped iniquity—and
you shall eat the fruits of treachery—because you relied on
your way, on your host of warriors."

[188] See *Hosea* 10:15 - 11:1-6, "This is what Bethel has done to
you for your horrible wickedness: at dawn shall Israel's
monarchy utterly perish. I fell in love with Israel when he was
still a child; and I have called [him] My son ever since Egypt.
Thus were they called, but they went their own way; they
sacrifice to Baalim and offer to carved images. I have
pampered Ephraim, taking them in my arms; but they have
ignored my healing care. I drew them with human ties, with
cords of love; but I seemed to them as one who imposed a
yoke on their jaws, though I was offering them food. No! They
return to the land of Egypt, and Assyria is their king. Because
they refuse to repent, a sword shall descend upon their towns
and consume their limbs and devour [them] because of their
designs." Bethel refers to the worship of golden calves at
Bethel (and Dan) established by Jeroboam, first king of the
northern Kingdom of Israel (opposed to the southern Kingdom
of Judah) after the fracture of the United Kingdom of Israel
under Saul, Eshbaal, David, and Solomon.

[189] See THE EXPLOITATION OF LIVE AVIAN
RESOURCES IN PHARAONIC EGYPT: A
SOCIO-ECONOMIC STUDY A DISSERTATION for an
in-depth dissertation on the exploitations of birds in Ancient
Egypt.

Let the fowler be utterly afflicted while searching out for the denizens of the sky. If the flock passes by above him, let the gods prevent him, for they are opposed to his activity.[190]

A fowler protested:

But Hathor, Mistress of the Sky, we have had snaring since the time of Horus, when Sekhet[191] came into being for us![192]

Hathor replied:

It is by the fowlers' nets and sticks that geese are force-fed and fattened, birds' necks are snapped, the voyagers of the sky are imprisoned in cages. How many millions of birds are sacrificed to Thoth, to pharaohs, even to me? And who profits by selling these offerings? – the very temples who praise me!

---

[190] See the Middle Kingdom ancient Egyptian literary work, *The Satire On the Trades*.
[191] Goddess of fowling, fishing, fields, and marshes. See The Goddess sxt in Ancient Egypt.
[192] See the Late Twelfth Dynasty (circa 19th century BCE) literary text, *The Discourse of the Fowler*.

How do you declare Amun to the fish in the
deep and to fowl in the sky, yet capture,
confine, and butcher these? Amun, who
gives breath to one who is weak and rescues
one who is in dire straits![193] Yet you are the
shepherd who knows how to give breath yet
takes it![194] You ought rather to warn these to
beware of you![195]

No god intended these extremes of
capturing, torturing, and wasting of life.

A farmer protested:

Hathor, Princess of the West, – don't you see
how we care for the mules and oxen. We
would be unable to raise our crops without
them. We have to treat them well or else
they will weaken and die. Then we will
starve and have to pay the temple in
recompense according to the leases.

---

[193] See the *Stela of Nebre* from the necropolis of Deir
el-Medina's workers during the reign of Rameses II.
[194] See the *Cycle of Songs in Honor of Senwosret III* for the
praise of the pharaoh as "our shepherd who knows how to give
breath."
[195] See the *Stela of Nebre* from the necropolis of Deir
el-Medina's workers during the reign of Rameses II.

Yes, some are neglectful of beasts, and they should be punished. But we mostly treat them well for our own and everyone's sake.

Yes, some of the beasts suffer; but so do we! As you yourself say — what would you have us do? If we refuse to plow or load the carts, what will happen to us?

We understand the suffering of beasts better than you – for we suffer likewise.

And how else do you expect to feed all the mouths of Egypt without the increases the strength of beasts enables?

And what of the mice, the snakes, the worms, the ants, and all you kill when you sow and harvest and thresh the plants? And what of these plants themselves? Are they not also nursed by the rays of the solar sphere?

A fisher protested:

Hathor, Lady of Byblos, the fish swim freely and we sometimes take them, just as the crocodiles and the birds live upon the fish. It is of little concern to a fish whether they are

taken by a human or another. So it has
always been. That's why they spawn so
many eggs.

And those we raise in artificial ponds swim
freely without fear of predators.

Again Hathor was perplexed. The people of Egypt
had flourished by their farming and the fields
plowed by her brethren. If they stopped relying on
animals for plowing and carrying, there would be
widespread famine.

How could she reply?

Again Hathor turned to Kamadhenu for advice.

Kamadhenu replied:

I address now the farmers as well as the
lessors of the land and cattle from the
priesthood and the palace.

Treat the working animal as you yourself
would want to be treated. Do not overburden
them. Do not interrupt an animal who is
suckling her child.[196] Care for them all like

---

[196] See the 1st/2nd century CE Hindu legal text, *Laws of Manu*,
IV, 59.

widows when they are injured or too old to work. For they have served you well and earned their reward.

Some will object, "But we must kill the plants by harvesting them. Even the plowing and tilling of the fields kills small animals and insects accidentally."

I reply: Yes, it is good to be aware even of this violence. But this does not justify killing more animals who consume these plants along with those harmed in the tilling and harvesting process.

For if the people would abstain from animal flesh and milk, you would not need to dilute your crops by first feeding the animals and then eating their flesh.

Much crops are wasted and an overabundance are killed in this process.

Instead eat only the plants and share the bounty with the animals–treat them at least as well as the foremen and scribes treat you–with payment and regular rest.

Thus you will reduce the suffering on yourselves and the cattle. Their share of the crops for their labors is as great as yours for your labors.

Kamadhenu added:

With the barley, wheat, sorghum, and other foodstuffs, plant medicinal herbs suitable for humans and animals that all may flourish.[197]

Yahweh added:

And when you reap the harvest, don't clear it completely to the edges of the field. And any parts that you don't initially gather should likewise be left in place. Leave these ungathered for the poor and the insects, animals, and birds to eat.[198] Consider these not thieves, but beneficiaries.[199]

---

[197] See *Edicts of Ashoka*, Rock Edict II.

[198] See *Leviticus* 23:22 and *Deuteronomy* 24:19-21 in which the god Yahweh commands this practice on behalf of the poor, fatherless, and widows. Hathor extends this benevolence beyond the human species.

[199] In the *Reminder of the Scribe's Superior Status (Papyrus Sallier I, 6, 1-9)*, the scribe tells of the remainder left after threshing being for thieves. This comes after talking about the mice, sparrows, hippopotamus, snake, locust, and cattle taking away the grain from the fields.

Hathor continued:

> Yes, and do not overharvest your fields. Let them lay fallow. Thus the worms and insects will be given time to live freely and thereby revitalize the soils.

> Do not waste crops by taxing them for the temples or burying them with corpses for the afterlife. Let the one who farms the land be lord of it or else leave it common for all. Consolidation of lands under ministers and temples serves only to starve the people and animals.

> So also with the so-called Sacred Herds of Hathor and those of other gods.

> It is but one more mode of their profiting through the toilings of humans and animals upon the lands they hold.

> Remove them from their hypocritic enclosures. Let the cows graze freely and unrestricted[200] on protected pastures.

---

[200] See Plutarch, _Life of Cato Major_.

To the Millers

To the millers, she said:

> You beat us to drive your millstone and
> grind the grains as the foremen beat you.
>
> And the priests and priestesses stockpile and
> waste your harvest in empty offerings. They
> tax you to fill their temples with gold and
> statues and offerings. They trade these
> goods and make themselves rich!
>
> You are under the yoke turning the millstone
> with us! You are crushed like the grains we
> thresh! Don't you see!"

A miller protested:
> Hathor, Mistress of Myrrh – how else could
> we grind the grains to bake in so many
> ovens of Egypt? Would you prefer that we
> lash people? Would you prefer that we
> starve? Why do you seek to deny us our
> bread?

Hathor replied:

> As Kamadhenu told the farmers and fishers,
> treat your work-animals like you want to be
> treated.

Do not overwork them.

When they are pregnant let them rest. When they give birth let them be with their children. Do not separate them once the calves grow up.

Do not urge them much with the goad[201] or brand them with fire when they are working.

Let them be without muzzles when they thresh the grain.[202]

And do not cut their throats when they are weak: weary of work, weary of heart, and weary of life.

And when they are old or crippled let them be cared for out of respect for the life, prosperity, and health they have provided for you and your people.

Some day humans must learn to plow their fields and grind their grain without the aid of cattle.

---

[201] See the 1st/2nd century CE Hindu legal text, *Laws of Manu*, IV, 69.

[202] See *Deuteronomy* 25:4: "You shall not muzzle an ox while it is threshing."

How could they possibly do this, you might ask? That is humanity's business to find out![203]

Painted cow skull from a Medjay "pan-grave" burial site in Abydos, Upper Egypt, circa 1640 – 1550 BCE

---

[203] Paraphrasing the vegan activist and inventor Lewis Gompertz (1784 – 1861 CE), who was a founding member of the Society for the Prevention of Cruelty to Animals and Animals' Friends Society.

Offerings to Hathor on a linen votive

Amulets of Hathor found in Amara West, Nubia (present-day Sudan).
New Kingdom.

To All Humans

Now Hathor inhaled and snorted seven times with blasts of her nostrils.[204]

To all the gathered humans, she spoke:

> At the very time that I am uttering syllables, beings are oppressed with evils. How long shall I cry, and you will not hear! I cry out to you of violence, and you will not save![205]

> You fear that your women are treated or described as animals. You know how savagely you treat us. And how cruelly you break and dominate human women.

---

[204] See *Exodus* 15:8: "At the blast of Your nostrils the waters piled up, the floods stood straight like a wall; the deeps froze in the heart of the sea."

[205] See *Habakkuk* 1:2, "How long, O LORD, shall I cry out and You not listen, shall I shout to You, 'Violence!' and You not save?"

See also *Habbakuk* 1:13-16: "You whose eyes are too pure to look upon evil, who cannot countenance wrongdoing, why do You countenance treachery, and stand by idle while the one in the wrong devours the one in the right? You have made mankind like the fish of the sea, like creeping things that have no ruler. He has fished them all up with a line, pulled them up in his trawl, and gathered them in his net. That is why he rejoices and is glad. That is why he sacrifices to his trawl and makes offerings to his net; For through them his portion is rich and his nourishment fat."

But during childbirth, who stands beside the wombed ones among you? And yet you forcibly impregnate me with your fists and arms shoved in my two rear-openings.

You steal my babies and their milk. You kill my sons and call their bodies veal.

Woe and abomination for the youth, small in age![206]

You force my daughters to repeat my fate and then kill and eat them.

Woe and abomination for the cows who will give birth to the youths, small in age![207]

You force-feed the goose and the cow. The smell of our burning bodies appetizes you.

I condemn you!

---

[206] See *The Prophecy of the Lamb* for this phrase, which is applied to human children in a time of social upheaval prophesied by a lamb, foretelling the overthrow of Egyptian rulers and a long period of foreign rule by Assyrians, Persians, and Greeks.

[207] Again from *The Prophecy of the Lamb*, though here referring to the mothers of human children, who will also be abused and taken away from Egypt under the foreign rule and strife.

You walk on skin sandals and wrap
yourselves in our remains when you are
cold. You know these are an abomination
and disrobe from them before entering the
temples. You paint your eyes with kohl
eyeliner made of animal fat.

I condemn you!

You kill quails and cows for your ancestors
– even dedicating thousands to me. What of
these cows and quails and their ancestors
and descendants? Who will intercede and
care for them?

I condemn you!

You hunt us for entertainment and think it
shows you as strong and powerful. It would
be much stronger for you to disagree with
your brethren who engage in such amateur
butchery[208] and recreational violence. You
capture and come upon us, slaughtering with
no pity![209]

---

[208] A term which Henry Stephens Salt uses to describe hunting
in his 1894 book *Animals' Rights: Consideration in Relation
to Social Progress.*
[209] See Ramses III's description of the defeated Libyans:
"Every part of their bodies is weak from the terror." Edgerton
& Wilson, p. 29.

We quiver in our bodies, our spirits
broken.[210]

I condemn you!

Your harp players pluck our guts as they
sing the ideals of my motherly love. Your
cruel songs mock us also with the beating of
rhythms on our skins. To these sounds we
are butchered and our bodies hacked up; our
great nostrils cease to function.[211]

I condemn you!

Meanwhile your own nostrils breathe the
scent of our burning flesh commingled with
the life-giving ankh which you depict
coming from my hand to give you breath.
You must rather give to us the breath, that

---

[210] See Ramses III's description of the defeated Libyans:
"Every part of their bodies is weak from the terror." Edgerton
& Wilson, p. 28.
[211] See Ramses III's description of vanquished Sea Peoples:
"Their nostrils have ceased to function, so that their desire is
to breathe the breath." Edgerton & Wilson, p. 41 and "They
that entered into the Nile mouths were caught, fallen into the
midst of it, pinioned in their places, butchered, and their
bodies hacked up." *ibid* p. 42.

we may breathe it; and life–that which is in your hands.[212]

I implore you!

You hope to rest and binge on flesh in the Field of Reeds. You imagine yourselves still hunting and torturing us there. This too is blasphemy and vexation. This heaven is not pure in my sight.

From Nebseny's Book of the Dead (circa 1500 BCE). He was a copyist in temples and palaces of Upper and Lower Egypt.

---

[212] See Ramses III's description of the words of captured leaders of his enemies: "Give to us the breath, that we may breath it, and life, that which is in thy hands." Edgerton & Wilson, p. 48.

Nebseny forcing cows to plow for him in the afterlife

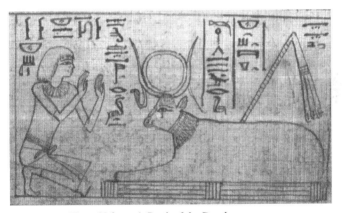

From Nebseny's Book of the Dead papyrus.

For many thousands of years in the past, slaughter of animals and cruelty to living creatures has increased.[213] What began as natural hunting of creature living upon creature has been perfected to an abomination by your administrators. Now we live in confinement. Every part of our bodies is weak from toil and terror.[214]

Look how you have killed the free-roaming cows and replaced them with subjugated, forcibly impregnated, castrated, desecrated cows who you control more profitably.

You were forced to do this by the elites who dominated your ancestors and theirs.

They control the land, the animals, and the humans themselves and exploit you all for their own status.

Throw off your yoke and those of your fellow beings.

---

[213] See the *Edicts of Ashoka*, Rock Edict IV.
[214] See Ramses III's description of the defeated Libyans: "The northern countries quivered in their bodies, namely the Peleset, Thekk[er], ... They were cut off from their land coming, their spirit broken." " Edgerton & Wilson, p. 30.

If you praise and appeal to me that I might hear your petitions to grant you your beloved,[215] do not deny the cows the right to choose their own partners! Some do not even know the bull whose semen is put inside her.

You praise me for bringing the fragrance of your beloved, yet declare your beloved to be skilled in snaring despite not being the child of a cattle breeder.[216] How can you make such comparisons in the same breaths while it is the fragrance of my burning children that overwhelms the temples?

If you look at me as the symbol of motherly love, do not steal, maim, and kill my children.

If you look to me for help in the Duat,[217] do not harm any beings.

---

[215] See, for example, the fifth stanza of *The Love Songs of Papyrus Chester Beatty*.

[216] See poem #43 from *The Nakht-Sobek Songs From Papyrus Chester Beatty I*.

[217] See also the Zoroastrian *Bundahišn 30*, in which the souls of the righteous are greeted by a plump, milk-filled cow upon welcome to heaven after being judged righteous.

Let us have life, duration, and satisfaction[218]
instead of torture and travails.

We beg peace of you![219]

And it came to pass, when Hathor spoke these
words, that the people lifted up their voice, and
wept.[220]

One among them turned to another and said:

Now that I have heard a voice for the
animals I pity them.

A visiting priestess of Gaia from Pytho, who was
born in Keftiuan Knossos, interrupted:

Oh, but you did not need Hathor to speak for
them!

---

[218] A common blessing bestowed on humans by the gods.

[219] See Ramses III's description of the defeated Libyans: "Let
us go to him! Let us beg peace of him! Let us kiss the
ground!" Edgerton & Wilson, p. 30.

[220] See *Judges 2*, 2:1-4: "An angel of the LORD came up from
Gilgal to Bochim and said, 'I brought you up from Egypt and I
took you into the land which I had promised on oath to your
fathers. And I said, "I will never break my covenant with you.
And you, for your part, must make no covenant with the
inhabitants of this land; you must tear down their altars." But
you have not obeyed Me—look what you have done!
Therefore, I have resolved not to drive them out before you;
they shall become your oppressors, and their gods shall be a
snare for you.'"

We deprive a soul of the sun and light, and of that proportion of life and time it had been born into the world to enjoy. And then we fancy that the voices it utters and screams forth to us are nothing but certain inarticulate sounds and noises.[221]

Cows are killed, butchered, sacrificed

---

[221] Plutarch, 'On the Eating of Flesh' I.4, in *Moralia*. Plutarch was a priest at the Greek Delphi. He visited Egypt and recorded a version of *The Lamentations of Isis and Nepthys* (referenced herein). The *Homeric Hymn 3, "To Apollo",* tells that Apollo transformed himself into a dolphin and brought Cretan priests from Knossos (political center of the Minoan/Keftiuan culture) to be his priests at this place of his oracular priestesses, temples, treasuries, and social center.

Bull horn wall adornment at the Minoan Palace of Knossos on Crete
(aka the Horns of Consecration)

Minoan terracotta bull, circa 1200 – 1100 BCE

A Wetnurse Speaks

A wetnurse said:

> Do not give your child to the wetnurse so as
> to cause that she cast out hers.[222] And do not
> wean the calf to nurse your children thereby
> from the cow. This too is violence.

> Do not abandon a cow of your herd when
> she does not become pregnant or give birth
> and milk.[223]

> The wet-nurses in the women's quarters
> determine the fate of their lord.[224]

Enslaved Humans Speak

Hathor spoke:

> I have gathered here among you some
> enslaved people. They are under my
> protection. I wish for you to see the
> similarities in the horrors of enslaved people

---

[222] See *The Instruction of 'Onchsheshonqy* (tentatively dated
to the Ptolemaic period) for this admonition. Late Period
Lichtheim.

[223] See *The Instruction of 'Onchsheshonqy*: "Do not abandon a
woman of your house when she does not become pregnant or
give birth."

[224] See the Sumerian *Instructions of Shuruppag* for this
admonition.

and animals. Do you not fear yourself or your spouse or children being enslaved? Imagine it. Now understand that this is the condition in which you hold the non-human beings.

Some among the enslaved people shouted:

Do not compare us to animals!

Do not preach to us and do not come after us.

Many of them departed

Among those who remained, one said:

Hathor is right in the comparison. It is right that it makes us uncomfortable. Such is the horror of the enslaved person's condition. And so it is for the non-human being. Like the enslaved person they are branded, castrated for subdual, have their ears clipped, are tattooed, cannot control their bodies, lack autonomy, have their children and pairs taken away from them and killed, do not get enough rest, have poor nutrition, do not control their sex and procreation, are transported, are bought, are sold, are stolen.

How can you steal our lives, our bodies, our minds? You cannot understand what we've seen. Why don't we just kill ourselves, you ask? Many of us do.

You think you understand. It's far, far worse. You sacrifice some of us along with them in your festivals. For us as for them you raid and seize from your neighbors. We are all put to work after forced marches to your lands. Many also die along the way.

More of the enslaved people departed. A few remained to listen to the rest.

Those who only eat milk, eggs, and honey

Some among the people spoke up:

Yes, Hathor, Beautiful of Cattle, Lady of Gebelein[225], there are so many cruel amongst humans. But we never eat the cows and chickens and goats and lambs! No, these support us all, so to eat them would be to eat everyone![226] We only eat eggs, honey, and

---

[225] See *"Hatshepsut's Speos at Gebelein – Preliminary Conclusions on the Unpublished Temple"* by Takács, Ejsmond, Chyla, and Witkowski.

[226] An argument made in the Hindu *Satapátha-Bráhman* attributed to the sage Yajnavalkya (circa 800 - 600 BCE): "Let

milk. This does not kill the beings. If only
more lived like us! How much less suffering
there would be!

Hathor replied:

I understand that you mean to reduce
suffering and commend you for it.

But what you do is perhaps worse. The
mothers end up being killed and chopped
and burned and eaten anyway after suffering
caged production and having their babies
taken away from them.

Once they become unprofitable as egg or
milk producers they get their throats slit just
like the meat ones.

---

him not eat the flesh of either the cow or the ox; for the cow
and the ox doubtless support everything here on earth. The
gods spake, 'Verily, the cow and the ox support everything
here: come, let us bestow on the cow and the ox whatever
vigour belongs to other species!' Accordingly they bestowed
on the cow and the ox whatever vigour belonged to the other
species of animals; and therefore the cow and the ox eat most.
Hence, were one to eat the flesh of an ox or a cow, there would
be, as it were, an eating of everything, or as it were, a going on
to the end (or to destruction)."

Like those who eat flesh, your stomach is
still a tomb for animals.[227]

Know also that abstaining from harming
these animals because of the benefits
humans get by them is misguided. Abstain
from harm for their own sakes, not because
of your own benefits.

Continue on your way and abstain from
consuming these products.

Those who abstain in fasting periods but not in dress and other ways.

Some others among the people spoke up:

Hail to you Hathor! Yes, there are so many
cruel amongst humans. We live as you say.
For two thirds of the year we eat neither the
flesh nor the milk, honey, or eggs. If only
more lived like us! How much less suffering
there would be!

Hathor replied:

---

[227] Paraphrasing a statement of the Jain priest Hiravijaya to the
Muslim Mughal emperor Akbar (1556 – 1605 CE),
contributing to the emperor's transition to vegetarianism and
banning the killing of animals for about half of the year.

I understand that you mean to reduce suffering and perfect your souls. I commend you for it.

Why do you not refrain for the other third of the year?

Some of these decided that after beginning their fasting the next day,[228] they would continue abstaining from eating animals and milk indefinitely.

Hathor added:

And who drives the chariots and carts? Whose skin do you wear when you are cold? If you mean to live without harm, consider the other ways you rely on violence to so many, even while fasting.

---

[228] In the Coptic Egyptian Orthodox Christian Church, the 43-day fasting of Advent (culminating in the celebration of Jesus's) begins on the 16th day of Hathor. During this time, one refrains from all food and water except from sunset to midnight. The evening meal must be vegan. Approximately two thirds of the Coptic Egyptian Orthodox Christian Church calendar is filled with such fasting periods. This book, Lament of Hathor, began on the first day of the month of Hathor. After two weeks for arrivals, we are presently on the 15th day of Hathor.

Those who abstain in eating, dress, and other ways but still sacrifice

Some among the people spoke up:

Yes, Hathor, oh glowing one,[229] there are so
many cruel amongst humans. We live as you
say. We do harm neither through diet nor
dress nor go from place to place. We partake
only of meat sacrificed at the temples and
give praise to you and the gods. Sacrificing
is not slaughter. For this do the animals
live.[230] Being sacrificed, these cows and
birds feed the gods, are themselves honored,
and participate in eternal life.[231] If only more
lived like us! How much less suffering there
would be!

---

[229] See inscription at the court of the temple of Hathor at Deir
el-Bahari.

[230] See the *Laws of Manu* (V.39): "Svayambhû (the
Self-existent) himself created animals for the sake of
sacrifices; sacrifices (have been instituted) for the good of this
whole (world); hence the slaughtering (of beasts) for sacrifices
is not slaughtering (in the ordinary sense of the word)." See
also the argument offered in the Hindu treatise on law and
conduct *Vashistha Dharmasutra*: "Meat can never be obtained
without injuring living beings, and to injure living beings does
not procure heavenly bliss; therefore the (sages declare) the
slaughter (of beasts) at a sacrifice not to be slaughter (in the
ordinary sense of the word)." (*Vashistha Dharmasutra*,
Chapter IV:7).

[231] See the Laws of Manu (V.40): "Herbs, trees, cattle, birds,
and (other) animals that have been destroyed for sacrifices,
receive (being reborn) higher existences."

Hathor replied:

> I understand that you mean to live a life of
> worship and reduce suffering and commend
> you for it. And yet you still make sacrifices
> to the gods and goddesses. You sacrifice
> hundreds of millions of cows, goats, and
> birds – their hearts brought to an end, their
> souls annihilated,[232] their eyes ceasing to
> behold the surface of the sun.[233] You most of
> all should know that your sacrifices are
> abhorrent.

> For I desire mercy, and not sacrifice;
> kindness more than knowledge of the rituals
> and spells or burnt offerings.[234]

---

[232] See Ramses III's description of defeated Meshwesh
Libyans: "They are slain in their places. Their heart is brought
to an end; their soul is annihilated upon earth." Edgerton &
Wilson, p.78.

[233] See Ramses III's description of defeated Meshwesh
Libyans and Meshesher, the son of Keper (their chief): "His
sons have ceased to behold the surface of the sun. His fighting
warriors are carried off as [lacuna] their wives and their
children – bound on their arms and their heads as captives;
their goods and their children heavy upon their backs; their
cattle and their horses brought to Egypt, taken away...."
Edgerton & Wilson, p.79.

[234] See *Hosea* 6:6: "For I desire goodness, not sacrifice;
obedience to God, rather than burnt offerings." See also
Matthew 9:13 and *Matthew* 12:7: "I will have mercy, and not
sacrifice..."

Do you think only of the gods during the killing and the cooking over fire, while the drops of fat drip? Or do you think of the animals' suffering? Or only of your own belly? Have you ever sacrificed just because you craved flesh, then made perfunctory rites?

The poor can't afford to be so cruel. Like the poor who fashion animals out of dough then bake and sacrifice them,[235] you may continue your rituals in a manner that does not harm any animals (except those who plowed the fields, carried the flour, turned the mill, died in the plowing, or were killed to prevent them from stealing the growing or stored grains). Or you may form clay figures of the animals and break or smash them to perform the ritual.[236]

---

[235] See Herodotus, *The History*, section 2.47. The Hindu legal text compilation *Laws of Manu* (circa 200 BCE - 200 CE) also states: "If he has a strong desire (for meat) he may make an animal of clarified butter or one of flour, (and eat that); but let him never seek to destroy an animal without a (lawful) reason." (*Laws of Manu*, V.37). See also the *Sankhayana-grihya-sutra* by Shankhayana (circa 500 BCE), which instructs the sacrifice of pairs of animal images formed from flour and jujube leaves (*Sankhayana-grihya-sutra, Adhyāya IV, Khanda 19*).

[236] See for example the Ancient Egyptian funerary ritual of breaking pots or the execration texts in which names of

Do not even offer burnt myrrh, for this
requires the stabbing of trees to produce
their resin. Trees also share their fragrance
when growing and living healthily.

If you mean to praise, live minimizing harm
and guide people to reduce and refrain from
violence against all beings. That is praise to
me.

A priest interjected:

But Hathor! We have always sacrificed. It is
by sacrifice that pharaohs of the past
ensured their entrance to the Field of Reeds.
Since it worked for them, it must still be
good for us![237]

---

enemies were written upon statuettes, bowls, or clay and then
destroyed.

[237] See the argument in the Vaishnavi Hindu text *Matsya
Purana*, Chapter 143 (circa 200 – 500 CE). The pious
mythical king Vasu is asked to moderate a debate between
Adhvaryu priests (who have taken pity on the animals they're
about to sacrifice) and the god Indra, to whom the sacrifice
would be offered. Vasu opines that (1) since the mantras call
for sacrifice and (2) because enlightened rishis performed the
sacrifice and reached the celestial abode Svarga (incidentally,
where the cow goddess Kamadhenu dwells), therefore
sacrifice is permitted and good. For this judgment, Vasu was
brought to a lower plane of existence (even though Indra
himself rules Svarga) for speaking with certainty on difficult

Hathor replied:

Do not be so sure of traditions and your own
righteousness. A priest must know that there
are multiple meanings in sacred acts and
texts. If you follow only the outer, literal,
meanings, you are missing the importance
and performing only futile acts.

I am telling you now that there is no
sacrifice without suffering and injury. This is
horrifying to me and heinous to the beings
you harm. Do not think about your eternal
life, but rather the lives of the cows, birds,
plants, sheep, and other beings you harm in
this one.

You will be judged on many acts by Osiris
and the 42 Assessors of Ma'at; not simply
whether you perform these inherited ones.

Tradition is not justification. Of yore,
pharaohs sacrificed their nobles and
servants. These too followed tradition and
did what they had seen and been taught by
their elders.

---

and delicate matters of dharma about which he should be
silent.

Many of those sacrificed did so willingly, believing that they would thereby be rewarded with eternal happiness. This too was tradition.

Eventually this was replaced with ushabti figures substituted for the actual humans. You may do this as well with the animals and even the milk, flowers, cakes, and grains you offer.

This will not happen all at once. There will be holdouts who insist on the killing. But each life saved is dear to the spared. Some may try abstaining from flesh sacrifice but still offer milk libations. Debate this amongst yourselves and recall that you too once performed these traditions when you grow frustrated or hopeless.

Minoan king Minos judging souls and assigning judgment within the eight inner circles of Hell (Inferno) in William Blake's depiction (1824 CE) of a scene from Dante Alighieri's Divine Comedy (1321 CE)

On the Negative Confessions[238]

Hathor spoke again to the humans:

> Do you only listen because you made me a goddess? Do you only listen because I speak in your tongue?

> Did you not hear my screams before? I know you did but you tell yourself I'm dumb and inarticulate. Did you not see the fear and

---

[238] As one of the steps towards securing eternal life, the deceased had to deny having done 42 types of evil things to assessor gods.

trembling and terror on our faces? I know
you did but you lie to yourselves. Did you
not see us struggle against your hobbling?
You saw and persisted. You should have
known without hearing your language or
seeing your goddess's body. It is clear.

Let Osiris, Anubis, the 42 Assessors of
Ma'at, and Ammit come forth.

Mithra, Zoroastrian lord of the wide
heavenly and earthly pastures shall stand
alongside these Assessors.[239] The Ba-soul of
the Keftiuan king Minos[240] shall stand here
too with these Assessors.

All of you humans and gods and goddesses,
look upon them and inside yourselves.

You will all be judged evil at the weighing
of your hearts. How many of the Negative
Confessions can you proclaim? Let us
recount but some you have broken.

---

[239] In the Zoroastrian *Hymn to Mithra,* Zarathushtra says:
"'The ruffian who lies unto Mithra brings death unto the whole
country, injuring as much the faithful world as a hundred
evil-doers could do."
[240] King Minos, the namesake of the Minoan civilization (as
named by British archaeologist Arthur Evans), was the
supreme judge of the dead in the Greek mythological
underworld Hades.

Can you proclaim "I have not mistreated cattle"? How many cows have been whipped, worked to death, confined, force-fed, trussed, and had their throats slit for your fancies?

Can you proclaim "I have not caused pain"? Can you proclaim "I have not made suffering for anyone"? Listen to the cries of the animals that cry and look upon the silent ones.

Can you proclaim "I have not caused weeping"? What of the cow whose babe you tie to the stake?

Can you proclaim "I have not killed"? Can you proclaim "I have not commanded to kill"? What of the butchers and priests you commission to slaughter? By them are felled thousands who know you not.[241]

Can you proclaim "I have not taken milk from the mouths of children"? What of the weaned calves whose milk you drink and offer as libation?

---

[241] See the *Cycle of Songs in Honor of Senwosret III* for this phrase.

Can you proclaim "I have not deprived the flocks of their pasturage"? What of the cows, sheep, and goats penned up or driven from pasturage to the slaughterhouses? Or those driven across the deserts that you seized from your enemies?

Can you proclaim "I have not snared birds of the branches of the gods"? How tortured are the ones whose necks you wring.

Can you proclaim "I have not trapped fish in their marshes"? How tortured are the ones you bring forth.

Can you proclaim "I have not driven away the cattle of the god's property"? There ought not even be cattle said to be of the gods' or anyone else's property!

Can you proclaim "I have not struck terror"? Look all around you. Look at the bull in the warpath, the cow in the pen, the baby wrested from their mother. The assessor Over the Old One will judge your treatment of all beings.

Can you proclaim "I have not been
hot-tempered"? Look how the drivers beat
us. Look how the children throw stones at
us. Have you not done similarly? The
assessor Disturber will judge your treatment
of all beings.

Can you proclaim "I have not been violent"?
Do any of you not live and thrive on
violence against us? The assessor You of the
Altar will judge your treatment of all beings.

Can you proclaim "I have wronged none, I
have done no evil"? We cannot count the
ones you have wronged. The assessor
Nefertem will judge your treatment of all
beings.

Can you proclaim "I have not cursed a
god"? Look at how you treat me and curse
my progeny. The assessor Serpent Who
Brings and Gives will judge your treatment
of all beings.

Can you proclaim "I have not slain sacred
cattle"? Do you not now see that we are all
sacred cattle? The assessor Blood-Eater,
who has come forth from the

slaughtering-block, will judge your treatment of all beings.

Let Anubis and Ma'aat and the Assessors know that most all of you cannot as yet truthfully assert even one of these negations. It is Falsehood who wishes to eat cattle, not Truth.[242] I will lead you all through the Duat when you die. And I will lead the children of your body and the children of your children's bodies that same way. I will not rebirth you and your descendents in the Field of Reeds unless you reform and can truthfully answer these negations from now until your first death. Ammit will eat your descendents' Bas unless they reform.

Let Thoth, Scribe of Hathor, re-examine his ledger and inform Osiris that all those who I previously re-birthed to the Field of Reeds must be re-examined to probe on their treatment of non-human beings. How many will remain in the Field of Reeds after this? How many will Ammit finally eat upon re-evaluation? The unjust must be unjustified!

---

[242] See *The Blinding of Truth By Falsehood*, written during the reign of Ramesses II (1279–1213 BCE) in the 19th Dynasty (1292–1189 BCE).

Let Nut's ferryman know that on behalf of
the living and the dead, on behalf of the
goose and the ox, I accuse you. Let Thoth
not carry you on his wings when the
ferryman heeds my admonitions.[243]

Let it be known that none of the future
pharaohs will be born of me or nurse from
my milk unless their parents, siblings, and
neighbors reform and sustain this world
under the sun so that all beings and plants
are treated with love and kindness.

Even if you only treat us kindly to save your
own souls, you must liberate us!

---

[243] See Pyramid Texts of Unas, Utterance 270, where the
pharaoh Unas summons Nut's "ferryman to ferry him across
the body of water that separated the sky from the earth."
(Lichteim, 1973, p.35). Unas states that no one alive, no dead,
no goose, and no ox accuses him of wrongdoing. Unas tells
the ferryman that if he fails to ferry him, Thoth will carry him
on his wings.

Long-Horned Bull, a knife-wielding cow god protecting the gate
named Powerful Of Knives in the heavenly Field of Reeds. From the
Book of Gates *in the tomb of Sennedjem (13th century BCE). See*
above for his and his wife's roles in the Hathor cult.

Neferti Prophecies[244]

Now there was a pause.

All the creatures who are oppressed with toils and distressed in mind by birth, life, and death, asked Hathor if this human awakening would begin the bliss of rest, saying, "Is this the end of our troubles?"[245]

Although Hathor could summon Bas from the past and the Seven Hathors could determine the fates of any individual, they could not foresee the future at large.

Therefore, Hathor asked the prophet Neferti to tell us of the future. A lamb stood beside her.[246]

Neferti spoke:

> Stir yourself, my heart, as we weep and look on what is to happen.

---

[244] See the *Prophecy of Neferti*.

[245] See Lotus Sutra Chapter 1: "And to the ignorant creatures who are oppressed with toils and distressed in mind by birth and old age, they announce the bliss of Rest, saying: This is the end of trouble, O monks."

[246] i.e. the lamb who gave the *Prophecy of the Lamb*, foretelling the upheaval and suffering brought on by the periods of foreign rule of Egypt by Assyrian, Persian, and Greek empires.

There is to be no divine or human savior.
And the gods become ineffective in
protecting the animals.

The cow is blocked from turning in both
directions,
The bleary-eyed mother is overpowered,
She is kept perpetually pregnant yet never
knows her mate,
A fist shoves semen in her vulva, assisted by
another deep in her rectum.
Her babies are torn from her, tied up, and
kept in tiny cages,
Her boy is killed and eaten as a tender
specialty.
The humans show off his soft skin draped on
their bodies.
Her daughter never sees the daylight as she
grows to recreate her mother's fate.
The baby's budding horns are burned off
after birth.
When she gives insufficient milk her neck is
split and her body carved, packaged, burned,
eaten, and discarded.
Those who refrain from flesh yet partake of
milk and cheese and skin help ensure her
fate.

Entire herds are slaughtered on grasslands
not to eat, but to starve, subdue, and
annihilate groups of people.

The pig is blocked from turning in both
directions; even while pregnant and
suckling, her children nurse through barred
cages.

The boy chick is slain by sharp crushing
tools after birth. His sister never sees the
daylight as she grows to recreate her
mother's fate. Some of her eggs are thrown
in jest.
Her feathers are ripped from her flesh; the
humans sleep peacefully on these bloodied
pillows. They are in the habit of seizing
chickens by the feet, throwing them upside
down upon the floor, pinching their necks
and using them ill.[247] When she gives fewer
eggs her neck is broken, her body is carved
and packaged and burned and eaten.

Those who refrain from her flesh yet partake
of her eggs help ensure her fate. Yes, the boy
chicks are ground up at birth, the laying
females have their beaks and feet trimmed.
They're stuffed in tiny cramped crowded

---

[247] See *Lotus Sutra*.

cages and go insane. They're bred to be too
fat to walk or fly or defend themselves.

The fish are gathered in great swaths.
Asphyxiating alongside them are other
beings of the seas not intended for the plates
of humans, caught up in greed.

The humans' plates overflow. They toss
some of the childrens' bodies and the milk
in the garbage. For this waste they suffered
and died. They are sent across the lands and
seas to be slaughtered or to shiver and starve
along the way. The ones suffering amongst
the dead cry out "I am alive!" yet are
crushed by the fall of bodies.

In their schools they carve up and poison
animals and fish and insects for curiosity,
education of healers, and searching for cures
of their own pains. This is done without
balms to first relieve their senses.

They affix pieces of dried skin on their robes
as marks of the vanities of their tailors. Yes,
everywhere you look there is animal skin.

Everywhere I see animals and fish
imprisoned in cells hardly their own size.

For leisure, they are lured with sharp hooks which slice their cheeks.

The Apis bull is stabbed in the thigh and cut across the throat.[248]

The last aurochs cows have been born and die without children. The last one's tongue hangs limp as his blood spills on the dirt of a Roman coliseum. He dies to the sound of thousands of cheering and jeering people. There will be no more on any land. Other types of cows carry on their fate.

The Nile is purged of hippopotami and crocodiles.

The sycamore trees are all felled and there is nowhere to nest.

Camels are burdened and beaten for travelers. Horses are made decrepit and mangy to pull carriages and killed when they become too weak. When they are weak they are no longer profitable.

---

[248] A fictitious crime of the Persian king Cambyses II (d. 522 BCE) while ruling as Pharaoh of Egypt and King of Kings of the Achaemenid Empire (550 – 330 BCE), as related by Herodotus (c. 484 – 425 BCE). See *The History*, 3.27-29

Cows and their milk are still eaten near your temples, with no thought of the lives they endured. Nor thought that some of these first bore the dairy cows' fates. They had been the wetnurses to the humans instead of their own children–then killed.

The seas and rivers are dying. The Nile flows with feces.

Neferti ceased prophesying. She then rose with recollection and consciousness, and forthwith addressed all the gathered humans, appearing to themselves as upon a mirror, "Do not tire· look at what is before you. Stand up to what is in front of you."

Now the gathered humans and human Bas bent their heads and whispered with each other.

Tracing of a panel of cow petroglyphs from Qurta (between Aswan and Edfu, present-day Egypt), circa 15,000 – 17,000 BCE.

Instructions of Hathor[249]

After Neferti's prophetic words and vision, the humans were silent.

Finally, one among them said, "Give us a word, mother,[250] that we may prevent this."

Hathor steadied herself then spoke these wise instructions:

> Do not despise a matter that pertains to a cow.[251]
>
> Give your ears and hear what is said,
> Give your mind over to interpretation:
> It is profitable to put these words in your heart,

---

[249] Instructions, or maxims, were a genre (known as Sebayt) of Ancient Egyptian wisdom literature. They often took the form of an official or pharaoh sharing wisdom with their child to guide them. Similar genres of wisdom literature were recorded in Sumerian, Babylonian, Hebrew, Greek, Sanskrit, and other cultures within the times and places covered by this book. In the European Middle Ages and Renaissance, similar writings were promulgated in the "Mirrors for princes" tradition. Hathor is often depicted as part of the design of Ancient Egyptian hand mirrors.

[250] This mirrors the sayings of the early Christian monastics of Egypt, whose writing often featured a monk asking their teacher for some wise saying by saying "Give us a word, father."

[251] See *The Instruction of 'Onchsheshonqy* for this admonition.

But woe to one that neglects them!
Let them rest in the shrine of your insides
That they may act as a lock in your heart;

In the midst of a community able to
command a profusion of delicious foods, it
ought to be deemed an affront to set dead
flesh before a guest.[252]

Do not unjustly eat what the water has given
up, and do not desire as food the flesh of
slaughtered animals,

Or the milk of mothers who intended its
pure draught for their young, not for nobles.

And do not grieve the unsuspecting birds by
taking their eggs; for injustice is the worst of
crimes.

And spare the honey which the bees get
betimes by their industry from the flowers of
fragrant plants;[253]

---

[252] Anna Kingsford.
[253] Abū al-ʿAlāʾ al-Maʿarrī

For they did not store it that it might belong
to others, nor did they gather it for bounty
and gifts.[254]

The motive of all must be Love, before we
can make life worth living.[255]

Do not expect utopia during your lifetime;
Not within thousands of years;
And even if it arises – will it not need
sustaining and protection?

No, but struggle for kindness in your time.
Keep the fight for those present.
Be inspired by those who called out for
justice before you.
Don't let their love have been in vain.

There will be setbacks in your time that
would be worse or longer-lasting without
your resistance.

Secure your strongholds where they now
stand.
Change conventions near to you.

---

[254] This and the previous four lines are from Abū al-ʿAlāʾ
al-Maʿarrī.
[255] Lucy Mallory.

Engage the temples, their priests and teachers, and the people directly.

Every step gained gives a better position for future advance.

Show respect for life.

Calm the weeper, do not oppress the widowed cows or other beings, and do not oust a person or other creature from their familiar lands, waters, and sky.

Beware of punishing wrongfully; do not kill or harm any creature, for it will not profit you.

Be kind to all creatures who are weak, and satisfy yourself with your own bread and drink.

Find fault with yourself, before another person does.

Provide for the people as for the cattle and the cattle as for the people, for heaven and earth were made at their desire.

The righteous care for the needs of their animals, the lands, and the waters, but the kindest acts of the wicked are cruel.[256]

Give to the poor among animals and humans rather than to the temples and pharaoh, who do not need your alms for their sustainment.

Instill your love into the entire world.

Provide sustenance for those in the lap of peace.

The gift of affection is worth more than the provisions that cover your back.

Teach according to the words of the wise.

You can educate children as you walk in the footsteps of the wise.

Speak justice, do justice, for it is powerful, far-reaching, and it endures. There can never be an excess of high standards, nor should there ever be a mean act to reach the humblest inhabitant of the universe.

---

[256] See Proverbs 12:10, "A righteous man knows the needs of his beast, but the compassion of the wicked is cruelty."

Do whatever opposes injustice to any creature.

Try, so far as you can, to wrong no creature, and keep your heart pure towards all of them.

Either live in kindness or lay down and die by starvation[257] to feed the land, bacteria, and scavengers.

Humans came after the cows and other beings who will outlast them.

Be zealous and strong in persuasion; apply yourselves to my lessons.[258]

Hathor ordered these words to be copied by her scribes and shared throughout the two lands. They were written in hieroglyphs, Hieratic, Demotic, Meroitic, Coptic, Akkadian, and the other languages written and spoken in Egypt. In this way, as many people as possible could read the words directly.[259]

---

[257] See the Jain practice of Sallekhana, the Hindu practice of Prayopavesa, and the Buddhist practice of Sokushinbutsu. In these, the person gradually starves themselves to death so as not to further injure any beings. See also philosophers such as Hegesias of Cyrene.

[258] See *Lotus Sutra*, Chapter 1.

[259] As Ashoka did with his edicts written in Prakrit (in the Brahmi and Kharosthi scripts), Greek, and Aramaic.

She also ordered for copies to be translated for Egypt's neighbors and trading partners as well as the priestesses and priests along with all the gods she gathered. And she ordered stelae and obelisks inscribed with them to be made in every nome of Egypt so that they will be remembered.[260] These stelae were placed before the gods in covenant.[261] She ordered that they be read before the people every year on the first day of the month of her name

---

[260] Similar to the mid-3rd century BCE *Edicts of Ashoka* (also containing prescriptions for kind treatment of animals) which were carved on pillars and walls and sent via missionaries to lands outside India. He sent some to the post-Alexander Ptolemaic pharaoh Ptolemy II, who likewise sent emissaries to Ashoka's Mauryan Kingdom.

[261] Like the silver tablets containing the treaty between the Egyptian pharaoh Ramesses II and Hittite king Ḥattušili III circa 1259 BCE after the Battle of Kadesh, ending years of warring. A thousand gods of the Hittites and a thousand gods of the Egyptians were invoked to consecrate and oversee the treaty. Copies were carved on silver and other stone tablets.

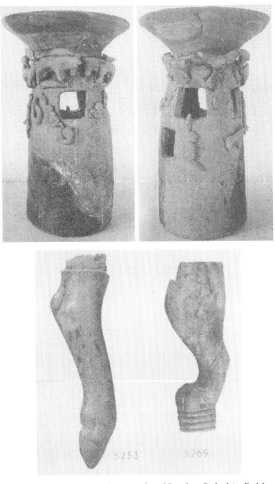

Votive offerings from the temple of Baalat Gubal in Byblos
(present-day Lebanon)

Bronze cow from Ras Shamra, Ugarit (present-day Syria), circa 1400 - 1200 BCE

Part Three: What Is to Be Done?[262]

Other Cow Goddesses, Gods, Priestesses, and Priests Speak

Now Hathor asked the cow goddesses, gods, priestesses, and priests from distant lands to tell of the treatment of cows among their peoples.

The Akkadian, Zoroastrian, and Croton priestesses and priests all lamented that their sacred cows had been foolishly slaughtered. They lamented that the people in their lands behaved much like those they heard Hathor address.

Those from Keftiu reported that while cows were venerated amongst the Minoans, they still ritually sacrificed and ate many of Hathor's brethren there. The priestesses showed the double-headed axes they used to split the cow's necks.

Those of the Canaanites and Ugaritics reported that their people also behaved similarly. They sacrificed and drove cows and other animals on their lands.

---

[262] See *What Is to Be Done?*, the novel by Nikolay Chernyshevsky published in 1863 CE. See also Leo Tolstoy's *What Is to Be Done?*, published in 1886. See also *What Is to Be Done? Burning Questions of Our Movement*, published by Vladimir Lenin in 1902.

They raided cattle from their neighbors. There was violence and no hope in their ways.

The priestesses and priests from the temple of Baalat Gubal brought terracotta, bronze, and gold votive offerings to place before Hathor in the cowpen.

Bronze animal figurines from the Temple of Baalat Gubal (goddess sometimes associated with Hathor) at Byblos (present-day Lebanon)

*Offerings encased in the multiple layers of the ground floor levels of
the temple of Baalat Gubal in Byblos*

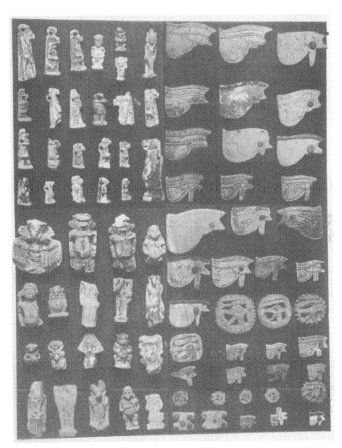

From the temple of Baalat Gubal in Byblos. Note the Eyes of Ra.

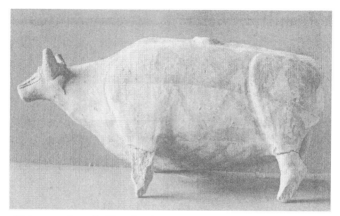

Votive cow from the Temple of Baalat Gubal (sometimes associated with Hathor) in Byblos (contemporary Lebanon)

Votive offerings in situ at the Temple of Baalat Gubal (sometimes associated with Hathor) in Byblos (contemporary Lebanon)

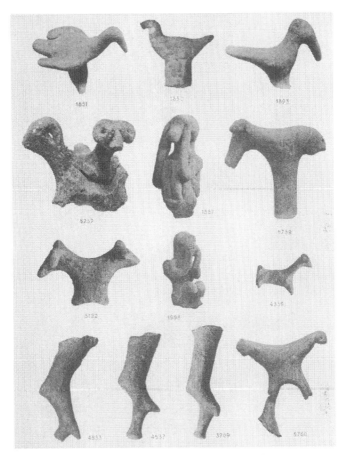

From the temple of Baalat Gubal in Byblos

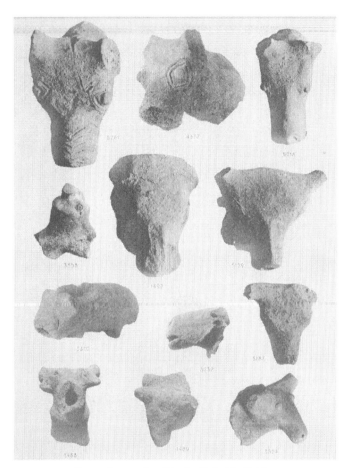

From the temple of Baalat Gubal in Byblos

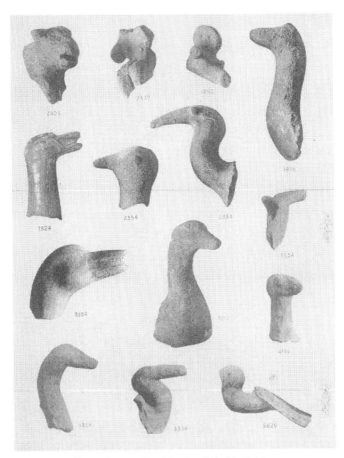

From the temple of Baalat Gubal in Byblos

The priestesses and priests of the remaining Egyptian cattle gods listened.

Hathor again wept.

Kamadhenu reported some intentionally peaceful treatment of cows amongst some of those who venerated her offspring in India. She said:

> Some among our people worship me and the cows. They feed and care for us. They punish others who harm us. They refrain from eating us.
>
> Some among our people abstain from flesh entirely, some consume only meat from sacrificial animals, others taste not even of the milk or eggs. And there are some who eat only plants that are not wholly destroyed in their picking.
>
> I heard you lambast those among you who abstain to certain degrees, urging them to do more.
>
> These are like rungs on a ladder. One does not climb the uppermost without first ascending the bottom. Let them be examples to one another and guide themselves to less

violence towards all beings. Though we desire complete abstention, any reduction is meaningful and lasting change comes gradually. So also there are some who are persuaded by arguments of dietary health while others are swayed by direct evidence of suffering. Some are converted to kindness out of fear for their eternal fate while others care for the suffering beings' own sakes. There are many skillful means by which people progress.[263]

Some of our kings make laws prohibiting and punishing various treatments of animals.

Some of our priests and priestesses share teachings and sing hymns instructing kindness towards all. Some say that I contain all the other goddesses and gods and that I therefore should not be killed.

Yet it is not all perfect in my land. The present age is still full of conflict and sin. Sacrifices continue. They still hobble us and separate us from our calves, who cry out for their mothers' comfort and milk. The ghee and milk libations drip with blood.

---

[263] See the *Lotus Sutra*'s discussion of many skillful means.

Some intend to show gratitude to the cows who plow their fields and carry their goods by celebrating festivals in their honor. Yet they paint these animals with irritating noxious dyes, place rattling bells and crowns upon their heads, and drag them around the villages rather than simply giving them rest.

I lament even to the King of the Celestials, Indra. I have told him of the suffering of my sons–how the plowmen strike them cruelly. Born of my body, I am filled with grief to see them yoked to the heavy plough.[264] I must return thence to oversee my children and brethren.

I will leave with you our humans' many writings advocating *ahimsa*, non-violence to all beings.

Kamadhenu and Hathor nuzzled. Kamadhenu lowed and rubbed heads with all the other cows gathered. Their priestesses and priests embraced.

---

[264] See Kamadhenu's lament to the king of the gods Indra in chapter 74 of the *Ramayana*, a Sanskrit epic from ancient India.

Amos icon from Kizhi Monastery, present-day Russia; circa 18th century CE

The words of Amos, a sheepbreeder from Tekoa:[265]

> I was no prophet, neither was I a prophet's son; but I was an herdman, and a gatherer of sycamore fruit:

> And the LORD took me as I followed the flock, and the LORD said unto me, Go, prophesy unto my people Israel.

---

[265] *Amos* 1:1.

Hear this word, you cows of Bashan on the hill of Samaria—who defraud the poor, who rob the needy."[266]

Proclaim in the fortresses of Ashdod and in the fortresses of the land of Egypt! Say: Gather on the hill of Samaria and witness the great outrages within her and the oppression in her midst.[267]

They lie on ivory beds, lolling on their couches, feasting on lambs from the flock and on calves from the stalls[268]

If you offer Me burnt offerings—or your meal offerings—I will not accept them; I will pay no heed to your gifts of fatlings.[269]

Spare Me the sound of your hymns, and let Me not hear the music of your lutes. But let justice well up like water, righteousness like an unfailing stream.[270]

These were the words of Yaweh, spoken by Amos.

---

[266] *Amos* 4:1-4.
[267] *Amos* 3:9.
[268] *Amos* 6:4.
[269] *Amos* 5:22.
[270] *Amos* 5:23.

Hathor Consults With Non-Humans and other goddesses/gods

The plants and non-human animals remained.

Hathor said: "We have made our case with the humans and heard of the treatment of cows in other lands. Now, let us consider and discuss our options."

Hathor reflected:

> If only we saw the end of humans! No more conceiving! No more giving birth! Then the land would be hushed from discord and turmoil would be no more. Yet humans desire to procreate. And so sorrow has come to be, and misery on every side. Such is the way it is since humans subdued us these last thousands of years. But will it end?[271]

> What can I do? Should I become Sekhmet and destroy humanity again - this time of my own volition rather than compelled by Ra? Should I let their blood flow and their cries ring out across Upper and Lower Egypt? No, I won't answer violence with violence. Violence has no place in the character of the

---

[271] See the Twelfth Dynasty (c. 1991 – 1803 BCE) *Admonitions of Ipuwer.*

just.[272] The humans must learn to live with
kindness for all. The gods can't just destroy
them every time they become oppressors.

Hathor posed the question, "Should we leave for
India?"

The animals, insects, fish, birds, and other beings
discussed.

> What would happen if we left? How many
> of us would perish by the journey? We
> would have to leave those of us not well
> enough to travel. Where would we graze in
> the Sinai or Midian deserts? We would
> travel through lands that abuse and sacrifice
> us.

> They would seize, hobble, and destroy most
> of us.

> We would prefer to be watered, fed, and
> abused by the Egyptians than to starve and
> thirst for water in the desert.[273]

---

[272] See the anonymous early Christian *Epistle to Diognetus*
justifying the non-violence of Jesus as God the Creator and
Fashioner of all things when seeking to persuade people to
faith.

[273] See *Exodus* 16:1-3: "Setting out from Elim, the whole
Israelite community came to the wilderness of Sin, which is
between Elim and Sinai, on the fifteenth day of the second

And what would happen to those who survived a journey to India?

The humans would make war to recapture us if we become scarce. Look how they subdue for gold and enslave people. So it would be for all beings of India were it to become a deposit of our kind. There would be sieges and assassinations to seize and bring us back to Egypt. Some of the corrupt among our protectors would traffic us for their own gain.

Many of the humans only torment us because they are tormented by humans above them. Would the farmer lash us if the overseer did not lash him? How would the milker live if they had to abandon their trade? Would the butcher kill us if the pharaoh and temples didn't demand it? And they have been told it is the will of the gods. These humans must also be liberated if we are to see betterment.

---

month after their departure from the land of Egypt. In the wilderness, the whole Israelite community grumbled against Moses and Aaron. The Israelites said to them, "If only we had died by the hand of the LORD in the land of Egypt, when we sat by the fleshpots, when we ate our fill of bread! For you have brought us out into this wilderness to starve this whole congregation to death."

No, this is our home. We were here before the humans even walked on two legs. We roamed freely for millions of years. Only a few thousand years have passed since they fully subjugated us. Prior to that they hunted us in the wild. Then we were yoked to the plows and turned over the earth. There would never have been a kingdom or even a nome or village of Egypt without the cow's subjugation. We still toil over the soil of Egypt, under a burning sun and a driver's lash. We live here–have lived here–have a right to live here, and mean to live here.[274] And for now we must suffer and die here. Let only a few hundred or thousands more years pass before the humans outgrow these ways or else come to destroy themselves in addition.

Hathor said:

My brethren, the time is no more when we control our fates. It is up to the humans now; they have subjugated us. It is up to them how much and how long we suffer. I cannot

---

[274] See Frederick Douglass's rejection of African-American relocation to Liberia in his essay *"Colonization"*, printed in the January 26, 1849 CE edition of his newspaper, *The North Star*.

protect you. If the gods had wanted to create a world where the humans did us no harm, they would have.

Eventually the humans will destroy themselves or learn to abide all beings. But the lowing herds[275] will freely graze some evening to come.

We are abandoned. We must persist.

Hathor Dismisses

Hathor again spoke to the humans:

I know that many of you will confidently try to prove that you have reasons for regarding your customs as legitimate and indispensable. You will say in your defense that authority is given by the pharaoh, the temples, and the gods; that the functions of the state are indispensable for the welfare of humanity.

But, however much you try to deceive yourselves and others, you all know that what you are doing is opposed to all the beliefs which they profess, and in the depths

---

[275] See Thomas Gray's *"Elegy Written in a Country Churchyard"*.

of your ba, when you are left alone with your heart, you are ashamed and miserable at the recollection of it, especially now that the baseness of your action has been pointed out to you.

Not a person of the present day can fail to know that all these actions are base and disgraceful, and that you need not do them. You all know it. You know that what you are doing is wrong, and would not do it for anything in the world if you had the power of resisting the forces which shut your eyes to the criminality of these actions and impel you to commit them.[276]

Hathor dismissed the humans of every class, except the priestesses and priests of her temples and those from the cow goddesses and gods of distant lands.

Other Cow Goddesses, Gods, Priestesses, and Priests Depart

The foreign cow goddesses, gods, priestesses, and priests now said, "We must support our brethren at home. Let our friends and followers spread the word."

---

[276] From Leo Tolstoy's 1894 book, *The Kingdom of God is Within You*.

Those of the Zoroastreans, Pythagoreans and the Hindu and Vedic peoples left copies of their writings and exchanged them with all before departing to their homelands. Nandi followed his mother back to the heavens of Goloka. Pigeons, a duck, and a hen carried papyrus copies of the texts home with them throughout the world.[277]

Votive offerings were exchanged amongst each others' gods, priestesses, and priests. The ones who had not practiced these substitutional sacrifices were given sets made by the Egyptian potters. They carried these back with them to their home temples and people.

Some of the priests of Serapis remained instead of departing.

On their ways home, all saw some of their own peoples heading towards Egypt following their initial departure. Among these peoples were more priestesses and priests, but also small trade caravans and companies of mounted scouting cavalry. Donkeys, mules, cows, birds, and fish sustained these all.

---

[277] See the magical tale *The Magician Hihor*, in which a duck and a hen carry a petition to the pharaoh on behalf of an imprisoned magician.

Now Hathor dismissed her own priestesses and priests and those of the Apis, Buchis, and Mnevis bulls, along with these cows and their families.

Some of these priestesses and priests walked out into the desert to live simply without violence instead of returning to the temples and their delicious foods. Others joined communities of women and men distinctly living suchwise six and seven hours by foot west of Dendera down and across the Nile. These refused to eat flesh or sacrifice either to the gods or the pharaoh as a god. Many of them lived only on bread and water and limited their movements to the confines of their caves, cells, and community confines. Some who joined these refused flesh foods for their own strength and denial but ridiculed those who abstained for the animals' own sakes

Hathor Returns to Her Duty

Hathor thought, "In their ignorance they will not heed the instructions I announce. It would be better had I never spoke. May my silent extinction take place this very day!"[278]

Hathor braced herself and again birthed the sun Ra in his beetle form Kheperu for Nut to carry across the sky. She knew that without daylight the beings

---

[278] See *Lotus Sutra.*

could not live. The beacon raised for a new first
dawn. The people saw that the Cow and the sun are
the best things to see with their good eyes.[279] By the
light and in the dark, Hathor inspects the progress
around the world. She looks upon the creatures and
their shadows. Every day she hopes to see
improvements and grieves with those who continue
to suffer

The Priestess Hathorhat Concludes

For a time there was no music in the Temples of
Hathor. No dancing in the Temples of Hathor.

Eventually, the hearers of the Lament of Hathor
began to go deaf. Weapons of torment were again
taken up. The cows and other beings of the land and
the waters and the sky lived and died again in
turmoil.

And the suffering grew and spread as prophesied.

And in her dreams Hathor sees the horrors. And in
her sleep she still weeps.

---

[279] See *Yasna 50* of the Zoroastrian Gathic hymns, in which the
symbolic evil-doer says that these are the worst two things to
see with his evil eyes. This evil one also cuts down the
pastures (see *Yasna 32*).

And she is apart from her brethren. Yet she still raises the sun.

Let this be a lesson for a million generations of people.[280] Let this book be a statue for Seshat[281] and Hathor. Remember the Lament of Hathor and let us hear the conclusion of the whole matter – Be kind to all beings: for this is the whole duty of us all.[282]

Thus ends the Lament of Hathor.

---

[280] See Rameses III's description of his victory over Meshwesh Libyans: "There was made for them a lesson for a million generations." Edgerton & Wilson, p. 79.
[281] Goddess of writing sometimes seen as a form of Hathor.
[282] See *Ecclesiastes*, 12:13.

Bibliography

All images by the author or in the public domain.

Special thanks to the podcasts Afterlives With Kara Cooney *(along with Jordan Galczynski and Amber Myers Wells, co-hosts; also of UCLA), and* The History of Egypt *by* Dominic Perry.

1. 1 Kings (Tanakh/Hebrew Bible).[283]

2. Amenemope. Instruction of Amenemope. *The Literature of Ancient Egypt.* Edited by William Kelly Simpson. New Haven & London: Yale University Press, 2003.

3. Ashby, Solange. Calling out to Isis: Interview with Dr. Solange Ashby.

4. Ashby, Solange. Sacred Dancers: Nubian Women as Priestesses of Hathor.

5. Ashby, Solange. The Goddess Isis and the Kingdom of Meroë. ARCE. September 20, 2020.

6. Ashby, Solange. The Kingdom of Meroë.

7. Asoka. The Edicts of Asoka. Trans. Nikam, N. A., McKeon, Richard. Chicago, USA: University of Chicago Press, 1959.

8. Astarte and the Insatiable Sea. *The Literature of Ancient Egypt.* Edited by William Kelly Simpson. New Haven & London: Yale University Press, 2003.

---

[283] All translations from the Tanakh/Hebrew Bible are from the Jewish Publication Society (JPS)'s 1985 translation.

9. Atharvaveda. Translated by Bloomfield, Maurice. Oxford: Clarendon Press, 1897.

10. Attar. The Conference of the Birds. Translated by Sholeh Wolpé. New York: W.W. Norton, 2018.

11. Avesta: Khorda Avesta: Niyayeshes (Litanes). Karl F. Geldner, Avesta, the Sacred Books of the Parsis, Stuttgart, 1896.

12. Ayali-Darshan, Noga. "The Other Version of the Story of the Storm-god's Combat with the Sea in the Light of Egyptian, Ugaritic, and Hurro-Hittite Texts", Journal of Ancient Near Eastern Religions 15, 1 (2015): 20-51.

13. Bailleul-Leseur, Rozenn F. The Exploitation of Live Avian Resources in Pharaonic Egypt: A Socio-Economic Study. Chicago: Doctoral Dissertation, University of Chicago.

14. Baraka, Iqbal. Al-Masri Al-Yawm (Egypt), August 22, 2018.

15. Bárta, Miroslav; Coppens, Filip; Vymazalová, Hana, et al. Abusir XIX: Tomb of Hetepi (AS 20), Tombs AS 33-35, and AS 50-53. Prague: Charles University, 2010.

16. Beaux, N., Caban, M., & Wieczorek, D. F. (2018). New foundation deposits in the Hathor Shrine of Tuthmosis III at Deir el-Bahari. In Z. E. Szafrański (Ed.), Deir el-Bahari Studies 2. Polish Archaeology in the Mediterranean 27/2 (pp. 51–70). Warsaw: University of Warsaw Press.

17. Blackman, Aylward. Apted, Michael. The Rock Tombs of Meir. Archaeological Survey of Egypt. Ed. Griffith, F. London: The Offices of the Egypt Exploration Fund. 1915.

18. Blackman, Aylward. The Temple of Bigeh. Le Caire Imprimerie de L'Institut Français d'Archéologie Orientale, 1915.

19. Bleeker, C. J. "Isis and Nephthys as Wailing Women." *Numen* 5, no. 1 (1958): 1–17.

20. The Blinding of Truth By Falsehood. *The Literature of Ancient Egypt*. Edited by William Kelly Simpson. New Haven & London: Yale University Press, 2003.

21. Book of Gates. Translated by E.A. Wallis Budge. London: Kegan, Paul, Trench, Trübner & Co., 1905.

22. Book of the Dead of Pajuheru.

23. The Book of the Heavenly Cow. *The Literature of Ancient Egypt*. Edited by William Kelly Simpson. New Haven & London: Yale University Press, 2003.

24. Breasted, F. H. Ancient Records of Egypt, Volume I. Chicago: University of Chicago Press, 1906.

25. Brethren of Purity. The Case of the Animals versus Man Before the King of the Jinn. Trans. Goodman, Len E. & McGregor, Richard. Oxford, UK: Oxford University Press, 2009.

26. Brunton, Guy and Caton-Thompson. Gertrude. Badarian Civilization And Predynastic Remains Near Badari. British School of Archaeology in Egypt and Egyptian Research Account, Thirtieth Year-1924. 1928.

27. Bryan, Betsy. Balachandran, Sanchita (Physical Analysis). "What Counts in Cattle Branding? Two Amarna-Era Brands from the Eton College Myers Collection." Wonderful Things: Essays in Honor of Nicholas Reeves, Peter Lacovara, Editor, 2023.

28. Bryant, Edwin. "Strategies of Vedic Subversion: The Emergence of Vegetarianism in Post-Vedic India", contained in A Communion of Subjects: Animals in

Religion, Science, and Ethics. Edited by Paul Waldau and Kimberly Patton. New York: Columbia University Press, 2006.

29. Bundahishn. Translated by E. W. West, from Sacred Books of the East, volume 5, Oxford University Press, 1897.

30. Colonna, Angelo. "Gods in Translation: Dynamics of Transculturality between Egypt and Byblos in the III Millennium BC." The Gods of the Others, the Gods and the Others Forms of Acculturation and Construction of Difference in the Egyptian Religion. Journée d'Études in Memory of Sergio Donadoni 84, no. 1 (2018): 26.

31. The Contending of Horus and Seth. The Literature of Ancient Egypt. Edited by William Kelly Simpson. New Haven & London: Yale University Press, 2003.

32. Crawford, Harriet. Early Dilmun Seals From Saar: Art and Commerce in Bronze Age Bahrain. Great Britain: Archaeology International, 2001.

33. Cycle of Songs in Honor of Senwosret III. The Literature of Ancient Egypt. Edited by William Kelly Simpson. New Haven & London: Yale University Press, 2003.

34. The Desert Fathers: Sayings of the Early Christian Monks. Edited by Benedicta Ward. New York: Penguin, 2003.

35. Deuteronomy (Tanakh/Hebrew Bible).

36. Douglass, Frederick. "Colonization", printed in the January 26, 1849 CE edition of The North Star.

37. Dream Stele (of Thutmose IV). The Great Sphinx and Its Secrets: Historical Studies in the Light of Recent Excavations. Translated by Selim Hassan. Cairo: Government Press, 1953.

38. Dunand, Maurice. Fouilles de Byblos. t.1, 1926-1932, Atlas. Paris: Libraire Orientaliste Paul Geuthner, 1937.

39. Edgerton, William F.; Wilson, John A. Historical Records of Ramses III: The Texts in Medinet Habu Volumes I and II. Chicago: University of Chicago Press, 1936.

40. Ejsmond, Wojciech. Archaeological Landscape of Gebelein in Egypt. IMOC PAS Archaeological Seminar. November 9, 2021.

41. The El-Amarna Correspondence: A New Edition of the Cuneiform Letters from the Site of El-Amarna based on Collations of all Extant Tablets. Translated by Anson F. Rainey, edited by William M. Schneidewind. Leiden: Brill, 2015.

42. The Eloquent Farmer. *The Literature of Ancient Egypt*. Edited by William Kelly Simpson. New Haven & London: Yale University Press, 2003.

43. Epic of Gilgamesh.

44. Epistle to Diognetus.

45. Exodus (Tanakh/Hebrew Bible).

46. Ezekiel (Tanakh/Hebrew Bible).

47. Fairbairn, Cannon. "The Nursing Hathor-Cow and the Nineteenth Dynasty". 10th Annual Birmingham Egyptology Symposium. May 25, 2023.

48. Fairman, H. W. "Worship and Festivals in an Egyptian Temple." Bulletin of the John Rylands University Library of Manchester, 1954.

49. Ferguson, Elissa. Slaughter and Lament: A Reconsideration of the Slaughtered Calf Scene. ARCE, 2022.

50. Fischer, Henry George. "The Cult and Nome of the Goddess Bat." *Journal of the American Research Center in Egypt* 1 (1962): 7–18. https://doi.org/10.2307/40000855.

51. Foltz, Richard. "Zoroastrian Attitudes toward Animals", *Society & Animals* 18, 4 (2010).

52. Förster, Frank. With donkeys, jars and water bags into the Libyan Desert: the Abu Ballas Trail in the late Old Kingdom/First Intermediate Period. British Museum Studies in Ancient Egypt and Sudan (BMSAES), Issue 7: September 2007.

53. Foucart, George. Tombes thébaines. Fasc. 3: Nécropole de Dirâ abû'n-Naga: Le tombeau d'Amonmos. Paris: Le Caire Imprimerie de L'Institut Français d'Archéologie Orientale, 1935.

54. Francigny, Vincent & David, Romain & de Voogt, Alex. Soleb & Sedeinga. Paris: Elnour Editions, 2014.

55. Friedman, Florence D. "Creating a King for Eternity."

56. Fuchs, Gerald. "Rock Engravings in the Wadi El-Barramiya, Eastern Desert of Egypt." *The African Archaeological Review* 7 (1989): 127–53. http://www.jstor.org/stable/25130513.

57. Gaber, Amr. The Central Hall In The Egyptian Temples Of The Ptolemaic Period. Durham theses, Durham University. Available at Durham E-Theses Online: 2009.

58. Garstang, John; Sayce, Archibald Henry; Griffith, Francis Llewellyn; Meroë, the City of the Ethiopians : being an account of a first season's excavations on the site, 1909-1910. Oxford: Clarendon Press, 1911.

59. Gilgameš and the bull of heaven. Electronic Text Corpus of Sumerian Literature.

60. Gillam, Robyn A. "From Myth to Taskscape: Animals in time and space in the ancient Nile Valley". TAG 2017 CARDIFF: Theoretical Archaeology Group Conference.

61. Gillam, Robyn A. "Priestesses of Hathor: Their Function, Decline and Disappearance." Journal of the American Research Center in Egypt 32 (1995): 211-37.

62. Graves-Brown, Carolyn. Dancing For Hathor: Women in Ancient Egypt. London, New York: Continuum Books, 2010.

63. Graves-Brown, Carolyn. The Ideological Significance of Flint in Dynastic Egypt. London: Doctoral Dissertation, University College London Institute of Archaeology, 2010.

64. Gray, Thomas. "Elegy Written in a Country Churchyard".

65. Greene, Joseph A. "Nuzi and the Hurrians: Fragments from a Forgotten Past": A Slice of Mesopotamian Life in the Fourteenth Century BCE. Near Eastern Archaeology, 61(1), (1998): 66-.

66. Hafsaas, Henriette. Cattle Pastoralists in a Multicultural Setting: The C-Group People in Lower Nubia, 2500 – 1500 BCE. Bergen: Birzeit University – Palestine: The Lower Jordan River Basin Programme Publications 10, 2005.

67. Hamilton, R. W. "A Sumerian Cylinder Seal with Handle in the Ashmolean Museum." Iraq 29, no. 1 (1967): 34-41.

68. Hammurabi. The Code of Hammurabi. Translated by Robert Francis Harper. Chicago: The University of Chicago Press, 1904.

69. Hardedef. Instructions of Hardedef. *The Literature of Ancient Egypt.* Edited by William Kelly Simpson. New Haven & London: Yale University Press, 2003.

70. The Hardships of the Soldier's Life (Papyrus Anastasi IV, 9, 4-10,1). *The Literature of Ancient Egypt.* Edited by William Kelly Simpson. New Haven & London: Yale University Press, 2003.

71. Harvey, Scott L.; Lehmann, Winfred P.; Slocum, Jonathan. Old Iranian Online. Lesson 1: Old Avestan. (Yasna 29). https://lrc.la.utexas.edu/eieol/aveol/10.

72. Heltzer, Michael. The Internal Organization of the Kingdom of Ugarit (Royal service-system, taxes, royal economy, army and administration). Wiesbaden: Dr. Ludwig Reichert Verlag, 1982.

73. Herd, Debora. Sensing Inequalities and Ancient Nubia.

74. Herd, Debora. Understanding Ancient Nubia from Antiquity to Today. January 21, 2023.

75. Herodotus. The History. Translated by David Grene. Chicago: University of Chicago Press, 1987.

76. HK6: the Elite Predynastic and Early Dynastic cemetery

77. Homer. The Odyssey. Translated by Robert Fitzgerald. New York: Anchor Books, 1963.

78. Hosea (Tanakh/Hebrew Bible).

79. Hsieh, Julia. Ancient Egyptian Letters to the Dead: The Realm of the Dead Through the Voice of the Living. Harvard Egyptological Studies, Volume 15. Edited by Peter Der Manuelian. Leiden/Boston: Brill, 2021.

80. Huyge, Dirk; Vandenberghe, Dimitri A.G.; De Dapper, Morgan; Mees, Florias; Claes, Wouter; Darnell, John C. First evidence of Pleistocene rock art in North Africa: securing the age of the Qurta petroglyphs (Egypt) through OSL dating. ANTIQUITY 85 (2011): 1184–1193.

81. Hymn to Mithra. Trans. Darmesteter, James, from Sacred Books of the East, Oxford University Press, 1898.

82. Ikram, Salima. Choice Cuts: Meat Production in Ancient Egypt. Leuven: Uitgeverij Peeters en Departement Oosterse Studies, 1995.

83. Admonitions of Ipuwer.

84. Jackson, Briana. Diplomacy through Shared Solar Theologies: A New Examination of Egyptian–Mitannian Relations. 2022-06-14.

85. Job (Tanakh/Hebrew Bible).

86. Gospel of John (Christian Bible/New Testament).[284]

87. Johns Julia, Patt Antonia, Hillmann Edna. Do bells affect behaviour and heart rate variability in grazing dairy cows?. PLoS One. 2015;10(6):e0131632. Published 2015 Jun 25.

88. Judges 2 (Tanakh/Hebrew Bible).

89. Kautilya. Arthashastra.

90. The Tomb of Kheruef: Theban Tomb 192. Trans. Wente, Edward F. Chicago, USA: The University of Chicago Oriental Institute Publications, 1980.

---

[284] Note: All translations from the Christian Bible/New Testament are from the King James Version (KJV).

91. Khordeh Avesta. Trans. James Darmesteter, from Sacred Books of the East, Oxford University Press, 1898.

92. Kiser-Go, Deanna. Three Generations of Ramesside Foremen Honoring Goddesses: The Case For Anuket and Hathor in the Neferhotep Family. Mural Decoration in the Theban Necropolis: Papers From the Theban Workshop 2016. Chicago: Institute for the Ancient Cultures of the University of Chicago, 2023.

93. Konrad, Kirsten. Sistrophorus Statues and their Ideological Impact, "Fifth Symposium on Egyptian Royal Ideology: Palace and Temple, Architecture – Decoration - Ritual", Cambridge, July 16th– 17th, 2007 in Cambridge, R. Gundlach and K. Spence (Hgg.), KSG 4/2, Wiesbaden 2011.

94. Gene Kritsky. The Tears of Re: Beekeeping in Ancient Egypt. Oxford: Oxford University Press, 2015.

95. Lamentations of Isis and Nepthys. Ancient Egyptian Literature: The Late Period. Translated by Miriam Lichtheim. Berkeley: University of California Press, 1980.

96. Lassen, Agnete. The 'Bull-Altar' in Old Assyrian Glyptic: a representation of the god Assur?. 2017.

97. Hoffner Jr., Harry Angier. Laws of the Hittites: A Critical Edition. Leiden: Brill, 1997.

98. Laws of Manu. Sacred Books of the East: The Laws of Manus. Vol. XXV. Translated by Bühler, G. Oxford: Clarendon Press. 1886.

99. Leviticus (Tanakh/Hebrew Bible).

100. di Lernia S, Tafuri MA, Gallinaro M, Alhaique F, Balasse M, Cavorsi L, Fullagar PD, Mercuri AM, Monaco A, Perego A, Zerboni A. Inside the "African cattle complex":

animal burials in the holocene central Sahara. PLoS One. 2013;8(2):e56879.

101. Lichtheim, Miriam (1992). Maat in Egyptian Autobiographies and Related Studies. Freiburg, Switzerland / Göttingen, Germany: Universitätsverlag / Vandenhoeck Ruprecht.

102. Liszka, Kate. "Pastoral Nomads and Travelers at Wadi el-Hudi." IKŚiO PAN: Borderscape Seminar. January 31, 2024.

103. Lotus Sutra. Trans. Kern, H. Sacred Books of the East, VOL XXI. 1884.

104. Love, Edward O. D. "Letters to Gods." In Jacco Dieleman and Willeke Wendrich (eds.), Los Angeles: UCLA Encyclopedia of Egyptology, 2023.

105. The Love Songs of Papyrus Chester Beatty.

106. The Magician Hihor. The Literature of Ancient Egypt. Edited by William Kelly Simpson. New Haven & London: Yale University Press, 2003.

107. Maimonides, Moses. The Guide of the Perplexed. Volumes One and Two. Translated by Pines, Shlomo. Chicago, USA: The University of Chicago Press, 1963.

108. Malville, John & Schild, Romauld & Wendorf, Fred & Brenmer, Robert. (2008). Astronomy of Nabta Playa. 10.1007/978-1-4020-6639-9_11.

109. Malville, John. "Climate Change, Nomadic Pastoralism and Astronomy at Nabta Playa, Southern Egypt."

110. The Man Who Was Weary With Life. The Literature of Ancient Egypt. Edited by William Kelly Simpson. New Haven & London: Yale University Press, 2003.

111. Matsya Purana. Allahabad: Apurva Krishna Bose at the Indian Press, 1917.

112. Gospel of Matthew (Christian Bible/New Testament).

113. Mehta, Shirin. "Akbar as Reflected in the Contemporary Jain Literature in Gujarat." *Social Scientist* 20, no. 9/10 (1992): 54–60. https://doi.org/10.2307/3517717.

114. The Teaching For King Merikare. *The Literature of Ancient Egypt*. Edited by William Kelly Simpson. New Haven & London: Yale University Press, 2003.

115. Micah (Tanakh/Hebrew Bible).

116. Moawad, Samuel. "Christianity in Dandara and Medamud." In: G. Gabra und H. Takla (Hrsg.), Christianity and Monasticism in Upper Egypt. Volume 2: Nag Hammadi-Esna. Cairo, New York: The American University in Cairo Press, pp. 89–96, 2010.

117. Modi, J. J. The Religious Ceremonies and Customs of the Parsees. Bombay: British India Press, 1922.

118. Moens, Marie-Francine, and Wilma Wetterstrom. "The Agricultural Economy of an Old Kingdom Town in Egypt's West Delta: Insights from the Plant Remains." *Journal of Near Eastern Studies* 47, no. 3 (1988): 159–73. http://www.jstor.org/stable/544958.

119. Monroe, Shayla. Ancient Pastoralists and Ancient States: The Political Ecology of the Nubian C-Group on Ancient Egypt's Southern Frontier. October 18, 2022.

120. Montet, Pierre. Byblos et L'Égypte: Quatre Campagnes de Fouilles a Gebeil (1921 - 1922 - 1923 - 1924). Paris: Libraire Orientaliste Paul Geuthner, 1928.

121. Morris, Ellen F. "Paddle Dolls and Performance." *Journal of the American Research Center in Egypt* 47 (2011): 71–103.

122. Mouton, Alice. "Animal Sacrifice in Hittite Anatolia." Animal Sacrifice in the Ancient Greek World, n.d., 239–52. doi:10.1017/9781139017886.011.

123. The Nakht-Sobek Songs From Papyrus Chester Beatty I.

124. Navile, Edouard; Hall, H. R.; Ayrton, E. R. The XIth Dynasty Temple at Deir el-Bahari, Part I. London: The Egypt Exploration Fund, 1907.

125. Negbi, Ora, and S. Moskowitz. "The 'Foundation Deposits' or 'Offering Deposits' of Byblos." *Bulletin of the American Schools of Oriental Research*, no. 184 (1966): 21–26. https://doi.org/10.2307/1356202.

126. Numbers (Tanakh/Hebrew Bible).

127. ʿOnchsheshonqy. The Instruction of ʿOnchsheshonqy. *The Literature of Ancient Egypt*. Edited by William Kelly Simpson. New Haven & London: Yale University Press, 2003.

128. Papyrus of Ani; Egyptian Book of the Dead. Translated by E.A. Wallis Budge.

129. Papyrus of Nebseni; Egyptian Book of the Dead. Translated by E.A. Wallis Budge.

130. Papyrus of Nu; Egyptian Book of the Dead. Translated by E.A. Wallis Budge.

131. Parkinson, R. B. "The Discourse of the Fowler": Papyrus Butler Verso (P. BM EA 10274). The Journal of Egyptian Archaeology, Vol. 90 (2004), pp. 81-111 Published by: Egypt Exploration Society.

132. Pavan, Alexia. The art of ancient South Arabia, portraits from ancient Yemen, symbolism and realism: the representation of animals, objects from temples and palaces, in Insights into the ancient South Arabia: The collection of the Museo Nazionale d'Arte Orientale "G. Tucci" in Rome, Pisa: Dedalo 2015

133. Pepi. Instruction of Pepi.

134. Petrie, Flinders; Griffith, F. Ll.; Gladstone, F. R. S.; Thomas, Oldfield. Dendereh, 1898. London: The Egypt Exploration Fund, 1900.

135. The Petrie Papyri: Hieratic Papyri From Kahun and Gurob (Principally of the Middle Kingdom). Ed. by F. Ll. Griffith. London: Bernard Quaritch, 1898.

136. Petty, Alice A. A Feast for the Eyes: Depiction and Performance of Ritual within the Sacred Space of Middle Bronze Age Ebla. *Critical Approaches to Ancient Near Eastern Art*. Edited by Brian A. Brown and Marian H. Feldman. Berlin: De Gruyter, 2013.

137. Philo of Alexandria. Philo: Volume III, On the Unchangeableness of God, on Husbandry, Concerning Noah's Work As a Planter, on Drunkenness, on Sobriety (Loeb Classical Library No. 247). Translated by F. H. Colson and G. H. Whitaker. Cambridge (USA): Harvard University Press, 1930.

138. Philo of Alexandria. Philo: Volume IX, Every Good Man is Free. On the Contemplative Life. On the Eternity of the World. Against Flaccus. Apology for the Jews. On Providence (Loeb Classical Library No. 363). Translated by F H. Colson. Cambridge (USA): Harvard University Press, 1941.

139. Pinch, Geraldine. Egyptian Mythology: A Guide to the Gods, Goddesses, and Traditions of Ancient Egypt. Oxford: Oxford University Press, 2002.

140. Pinch, Geraldine. Votive Offerings to Hathor. Oxford: Griffith Institute & Ashmolean Museum, 1993.

141. Plutarch. Isis and Osiris. From *Moralia*, volume V. Cambridge: Loeb Classical Library, 1936.

142. Plutarch. Life of Cato Major in The Parallel Lives, translated by Perrin, Bernadotte. Cambridge, MA, USA: Harvard University Press, 1914.

143. Plutarch. On the Eating of Flesh. Plutarch's Three Treatises on Animals. Trans. Newmyer, Stephen T. London: Routledge. 2021.

144. Pongratz-Leisten, Beate. 2021. The Animated Temple and Its Agency in the Urban Life of the City in Ancient Mesopotamia. Religions 12: 638.

145. Pongratz-Leisten, Beate. Comments on the Translatability of Divinity: Cultic and Theological Responses to the Presence of the Other in the Ancient near East. Corinne Bonnet, Amandine Declercq, Iwo Slobodzianek (ed.), Les représentations des dieux des autres. Colloque de Toulouse, 9-11 décembre 2010. Supplemento a Mythos, 2. Caltanissetta: Salvatore Sciascia Editore, 2011.

146. Pongratz-Leisten, Beate. "Conceptualizing Divinity Between Cult and Theology in the Ancient Near East." Pp. 619-654 in Dieux, rois et capitales dans le Proche-Orient ancien. Compte rendu de la LXVe Rencontre Assyriologique Internationale (Paris, 8-12 jiullet 2019). Publications de l'Institut du Proche-Orient ancien du Collège de France (PIPOAC) 5. Eds. M. Béranger, F. Nebiolo & N. Ziegler. Leuven/Paris/Bristol: Peeters, 2021.

147. Pongratz-Leisten, Beate. *Sacred Marriages and the Transfer of Divine Knowledge: Alliances between the Gods and the King in Ancient Mesopotamia.*

148. Prophecy of Neferti. *The Literature of Ancient Egypt.* Edited by William Kelly Simpson. New Haven & London: Yale University Press, 2003.

149. Ptahhotep. Instructions of Ptahhotep. *The Literature of Ancient Egypt.* Edited by William Kelly Simpson. New Haven & London: Yale University Press, 2003.

150. The Prophecy of the Lamb. *The Literature of Ancient Egypt.* Edited by William Kelly Simpson. New Haven & London: Yale University Press, 2003.

151. Pyramid Texts of Unas. *Ancient Egyptian Literature: The Old and Middle Kingdoms.* Translated by Miriam Lichtheim. Berkeley: University of California Press, 1973.

152. Reade, Julian. "The Ishtar Temple at Nineveh." *Iraq* 67, no. 1 (2005): 347–90.

153. Reminder of the Scribe's Superior Status (Papyrus Sallier I, 6, 1-9). *The Literature of Ancient Egypt.* Edited by William Kelly Simpson. New Haven & London: Yale University Press, 2003.

154. Richter, Barbara Ann. *On the Heels of the Wandering Goddess: The Myth and the Festival at the Temples of the Wadi el-Hallel and Dendera.* 8. Ägyptologische Tempeltagung: Interconnections between Temples, in Königtum, Staat und Gesellschaft Früher Hochkulturen 3,3, Wiesbaden: Harrassowitz, 2010.

155. Richter, Barbara Ann. *The Theology of Hathor of Dendera: Aural and Visual Scribal Techniques in the Per-wer Sanctuary.* University of California, Berkeley. Dissertation. 2012.

156. Rigopoulos, Antonio. "The Construction of a Cultic Center through Narrative: The Founding Myth of the Village of Puttaparthi and Sathya Sāī Bābā". History of Religions Vol. 54, No. 2 (November 2014), pp. 117-150. Published By: The University of Chicago Press.

157. Rilly, Claude. "The QSAP Programme on the Temple of Queen Tiye in Sedeinga." London: Sudan Archaeological Research Society (SARS), 2018.

158. Robins, Andrew. "The Alpha Hypothesis: Did Lateralized Cattle-Human Interactions Change the Script for Western Culture?." Animals : an open access journal from MDPI vol. 9,9 638. 31 Aug. 2019, doi:10.3390/ani9090638.

159. Rowan, Kirsty. Meroitic – a phonological investigation. School of Oriental and African Studies (SOAS), London. Doctoral Dissertation. 2006.

160. Rutherford, Ian. "The Reception of Egyptian Animal Sacrifice in Greek Writers: Ethnic Stereotyping or Transcultural Discourse?*." Chapter. In Animal Sacrifice in the Ancient Greek World, edited by Sarah Hitch and Ian Rutherford, 253–66. Cambridge: Cambridge University Press, 2017.

161. Sad Dar. Translated by E. W. West, from Sacred Books of the East, volume 24. Oxford: Clarendon Press, 1885.

162. Sahidic Fragments of the Life of the Virgin. Texts and Studies: Contributions to Biblical and Patristic Literature, Vol. IV, No. 2. Coptic Apocryphal Gospels. Ed. J. Armitage Robinson. Cambridge: Cambridge University Press, 1896.

163. Salt, Henry Stephens. Animals' Rights: Considered in Relation to Social Progress. New York, London: Macmillan & Co: 1894.

164. Sasson, Jack M. From the Mari Archives.

165. The Satire On the Trades. *The Literature of Ancient Egypt.* Edited by William Kelly Simpson. New Haven & London: Yale University Press, 2003.

166. Sayce, A. H. "The Astarte Papyrus and the Legend of the Sea." *The Journal of Egyptian Archaeology* 19, no. 1/2 (1933): 56–59. https://doi.org/10.2307/3854858.

167. Schwartz, Martin. "Gathic Compositional History, Y 29, and Bovine Symbolism". Chapter 10 in Siamak Adhami (ed.), Paitimāna, V. 2, Costa Meza, CA: Mazda Publishers, 2003.

168. Service des Antiquités de l'Égypte. Annales du Service des Antiquités de l'Égypte: Vol 59. Cairo: l'Institut français d'archéologie orientale, 1966.

169. Severus ibn al-Muqaffa, History of the Patriarchs of the Coptic church of Alexandria (1904) Part 1: St. Mark - Theonas (300 AD). Paris: Patrologia Orientalis, 1903.

170. Shaik al-Arab, Walid and Y. Ali, Ehab. Goddess Hatmehyt in Dendara Temple. Journal Volume (7), No. (2) September 2013.

171. Shankhayana. Sankhayana-grihya-sutra. Translated by Hermann Oldenberg, from Sacred Books of the East, volume 29. Oxford: Clarendon Press, 1886.

172. The Instructions of Shuruppak. The Electronic Text Corpus of Sumerian Literature. Accessed February 12, 2024.

173. Siclus, Diodorus. Library of History, Volume I: Books 1-2.34. Translated by C. H. Oldfather. Loeb Classical Library 279. Cambridge, MA: Harvard University Press, 1933.

174. Skjærvø, Prods Oktor. The Spirit of Zoroastrianism. New Haven & London: Yale University Press, 2011.

175. The Song of the Harper. *The Literature of Ancient Egypt.* Edited by William Kelly Simpson. New Haven & London: Yale University Press, 2003.

176. Staring, N.T.B.. "The Tomb of Ptahemwia, 'Great Overseer of Cattle' and 'Overseer of the Treasury of the Ramesseum', at Saqqara *." *The Journal of Egyptian Archaeology* 102 (2016): 145 - 170.

177. Stela of Nebre. *The Literature of Ancient Egypt.* Edited by William Kelly Simpson. New Haven & London: Yale University Press, 2003.

178. Stela of Neferabu. *The Literature of Ancient Egypt.* Edited by William Kelly Simpson. New Haven & London: Yale University Press, 2003.

179. Takács, Daniel; Ejsmond, Wojciech; Chyla, Julia; and Witkowski, Piotr. "Hatshepsut's Speos at Gebelein – Preliminary Conclusions on the Unpublished Temple". Göttinger Miszellen - Beiträge zur ägyptologischen Diskussion, vol. 247 (2015) p. 117-120.

180. Tantamani. Stela of the Dream.

181. Tebtunis Papyri, Part I. Translated by Grenfell, Bernard P. (Bernard Pyne), ed; Hunt, Arthur S. (Arthur Surridge), joint ed; Smyly, J. Gilbart (Josiah Gilbart, joint ed; Goodspeed, Edgar J. (Edgar Johnson), joint ed; Edgar, C. C. (Campbell Cowan), joint ed; Egypt Exploration Society. Graeco-Roman Branch. London, New York: Oxford University Press, 1902.

182. Tolstoy, Leo. The Kingdom of God is Within You. 1894.

183. Treaty Between the Hittites and Egyptians.

184. Twiss, Katheryn C., and Russell, Nerisss. "Taking The Bull By The Horns: Ideology, Masculinity, And Cattle Horns At Çatalhöyük (Turkey)." *Paléorient* 35, no. 2 (2009): 19–32. http://www.jstor.org/stable/41496866.

185. Valmiki, Maharishi. Ramayana. Trans. Shastri, Hari Prasad. London: Shanti Sadan. 1952.

186. Van Neer, Wim; Gonzalez, Jérôme. "A Late Period fish deposit at Oxyrhynchus (el-Bahnasa, Egypt)". Published in *Animals: Cultural Identifiers in Ancient Societies?*. Edited by Joris Peters, George McGlynn and Veronika Goebel. Verlag Marie Leidorf GmbH. Rahden/Westf.2019

187. Vashistha (attributed). Vashistha Dharmasutra. Translated by Georg Bühler. Oxford: Clarendon Press, 1882.

188. Vedic Hymns, Part I: Hymns to the Maruts, Rudra, Vâyu and Vâta. Translated by F. Max Müller. Clarendon: Oxford University Press, 1891.

189. Vyasa, Krishna-Dwaipayana. Mahabharata, Book 12: Santi Parva. Translated by Ganguli, Kisari Mohan. Calcutta: Munshiram Manoharlal Publishers, 1883 – 1896.

190. Wasmuth, Melanie and Ögüt, Birgül. A Syro-Hittite Weather-God in Egypt? Proceedings of the 6th International Congress on the Archaeology of the Ancient Near East May, 5th-10th 2008, "Sapienza" - Università di Roma Volume 1 Near Eastern Archaeology in the Past, Present and Future. Heritage and Identity Ethnoarchaeological and Interdisciplinary Approach, Results and Perspectives Visual Expression and Craft Production in the Definition of Social Relations and Status Edited by Paolo Matthiae, Frances Pinnock, Lorenzo Nigro and Nicolò Marchetti with the collaboration of Licia Romano. Wiesbaden: Harrassowitz Verlag, 2010.

191. Westcar Papyrus. Ancient Egyptian Literature: A Book of Readings, Volume I: The Old and Middle Kingdoms.

Translated by Miriam Lichtheim. Berkeley: University of California Press, 2006.

192. Williams, Bruce Beyer. A-Group, C-Group, Pan Grave, New Kingdom, and X-Group Remains From Cemeteries A-G and Rock Shelters. The University of Chicago Oriental Institute Nubian Expedition Volume X. Ed. Holland, Thomas A. Chicago: The Oriental Institute of the University of Chicago. 1993.

193. Winlock, H. E. Excavations At Deir El Bahari: 1911-1931. New York: The Macmillan Company, 1942.

194. Yajnavalkya. Satapátha-Brâhman, Part II: Books III and IV. Translated by Julius Eggeling. Oxford: Clarendon Press, 1885.

195. Yaron, Reuven. The Laws of Eshnunna. Jerusalem/Leiden: The Magnes Press, The Hebrew University, E. J. Brill, 2nd edition, 1988.

196. Zahran, M.A. (2009). Hydrophytes of the Nile in Egypt. In: Dumont, H.J. (eds) The Nile. Monographiae Biologicae, vol 89. Springer, Dordrecht.

197. Zarathustra. The Gāthās of Zarahustra. Translated by Insler, S., Leiden: E. J. Brill. 1975.

198. Zechariah (Tanakh/Hebrew Bible).

199. Zernecke, Anna Elise. "The Lady of the Titles: The Lady of Byblos and the Search for Her 'True Name.'" *Die Welt Des Orients* 43, no. 2 (2013): 226–42.

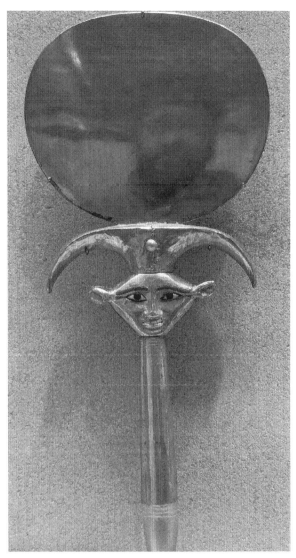

Author's selfie in a Hathor-headed mirror at the Metropolitan Museum of Art, New York

Author's selfie in another Hathor-headed mirror at the Metropolitan Museum of Art, New York